PHYSICAL EDUCATION

B.A. Third Year

Dr. Jitender Thakur
Assistant Professor, Physical Education
Government College RKMV Shimla
Himachal Pradesh

Dr. Shashi Kiran
Assistant Professor, Physical education
Government College Rajgarh Sirmour
Himachal Pradesh

Dr. Vikrant Bhardwaj
Coach/Assistant Professor
Directorate of physical Education and
Youth Program Himachal Pradesh University
Summer hill Shimla -171005

KHEL SAHITYA KENDRA
7/26, Ansari Road, Daryaganj
New Delhi – 110002

Published by:

KHEL SAHITYA KENDRA

7/26, Ansari Road, Darya Ganj, New Delhi – 110002

Ph.: (O) 011-65190343, 43551324, 42564726,
(M) 9811088729, (Fax) 011-42564726

E-mail: khelsahitya@rediffmail.com

ISBN:– 978-93-5877-239-5

PRINTED IN INDIA 2025

Laser Typeset by:
JAIN MEDIA GRAPHICS,
Delhi – 110035.

Printed at:
ASIAN OFFSET PRINTERS

CONTENT-- B.A. Year-III

THEORY COURSE

Course Code: PED305TH – Recreation

Unit-I-- Introduction

- Meaning of Recreation, aims and objectives of Recreation.
- Physical education and recreation.
- Need and importance of recreation in modern age.
- Arrangement of recreation centres.

Unit-II-- Camping

- Concept and meaning of camp, aims and objectives of camp.
- Types of camp.
- Agencies promoting camp.
- Educative value of camp.

Unit-III-- Recreational Activities

- Types and nature of recreation.
- Recreation providing agencies and recent changes in the recreational activities.
- Responsibilities of a recreational manager.

Unit-IV-- Picnic

- Meaning, importance and utilities of picnic.
- Organization of picnic and essentials for picnic and factors affecting its organization.
- Educative value of picnic.
- Recreational and Adventurous Avenues in Himachal Pradesh (Water Games, Paragliding, Winter Games, Mountaineering and Trekking).

THEORY COURSE

Course Code: PED306TH – Kinesiology and Biomechanics

Unit-I-- Introduction of Kinesiology and Biomechanics

- Meaning and importance of Kinesiology.

- Meaning and importance of Biomechanics.
- Joints, their types and movements around joints and Goniometry.

Unit-II-- Axis and Planes

- Fundamental anatomical position, planes and axis.
- Kinesiological classification of muscles.
- Role of different muscles: Agonist, Antagonist, Mover, Stabilizer, Fixator and Neutralizer.

Unit-III-- Biomechanical Terms

- Description of biomechanical terms: Distance, Displacement, Speed, Velocity, Acceleration, Angular Velocity, Angular Acceleration, Linear and Angular Motion, Kinetics and Kinematics, Force, Pressure, Gravity, Friction, Work , Power, Torque and Parabolic Path.

Unit-IV-- Motion and Levers

- Newton's Laws of Motion and their implication in sports.
- Mechanical Levers and their Implication in sports and physical education.
- Meaning and concept of Equilibrium and Centre of Gravity.

THEORY COURSE

Course Code: PED307TH – Methods of Teaching in Physical Education

Unit-I-- Introduction

- Meaning and importance of methods of teaching in Physical Education.
- Principles of teaching methods and different methods of teaching.
- Factors affecting teaching methods.
- Lesson Planning: Lesson plan, objectives and types of lesson plan.
- Principles of lesson plan and values of lesson plan.
- Class activity/Recreational part (Assembly, Revision, Reassembly and Dismissal).

Unit-II-- Teaching Aids

- Teaching aids, meaning, its importance in physical education, types of teaching aids and use and improvisation of apparatus.

- Presentation technique, criterion of presentation technique and qualities of good presenter.
- Factors influencing presentation technique.

Unit-III-- Introduction of Teaching Skills

1. Teaching Skills:

i) Lecture method.
ii) Command method.
iii) Discussion method.
iv) Project method.
v) Demonstration method.
vi) Imitation method.

Unit-IV-- Class Formation

- Class formation, its values and types of class formation.
- Supervision and inspection of teaching methods.
- Methods of supervision and qualities of a supervisor.
- Evaluation of teaching methods.
- Need and importance of evaluation

THEORY COURSE

Course Code: PED308TH – Officiating and Coaching

Unit-I-- Introduction

- Introduction of officiating and coaching and its importance in games and sports.
- Principles of officiating and coaching.
- Outlook of officials and coaches towards management, players and spectators.
- Measures for improving the standards of officiating and coaching.

Unit-II-- Coaching

- Philosophy of coaching.
- Coach as a Mentor, duties of a coach in general- Pre, during and post-game situations and responsibilities of a coach on and off the field.
- Psychological aspects during competition and coaching.

Unit-III-- Duties of Official

- Philosophy of officiating.
- Duties of official in general, pre, during and post-game situations.
- Technical and Tactical preparation of an official.
- Ethics of officiating.

Unit-IV-- Qualities and qualification of Coach and Official

- Qualities and qualification of an efficient coach and official.
- Current status of coaching and officiating in India.
- Measures for improving the standard of coaching and officiating in India.
- Role of impartial officiating and coaching in maintaining integrity and values of sports.
- Technical Officials levels and Exams of various Games (An Introduction).

PRACTICAL COURSE

Course Code: PED301PR – Specialization in Volleyball

Unit-I

1. History of game, measurement and preparation of the play field and equipment required for game.
2. Fundamental skills and lead-up games.
3. Techniques, strategies and method of play.
4. Rules and regulations of the game.
5. National and International tournaments associated with the game.
6. Team/Individual records (World, Olympic, Asian and National Level) of the game.
7. Awards associated with the game.
8. Duties of the officials.
9. Technical Equipment for officiating.
10. Knowledge of the score sheets.
11. Signals of officiating.

Unit-II

1. General and specific warming-up and cooling down.

2. Long-term and short-term preparation for the decisive volleyball competitions. 3. Psychological qualities and preparation of a vollcyball player.
4. Offensive, defense system in play, service and reception pattern.
5. Individual, group and team tactics.
6. Diet and nutrition for a volleyball player.
7. Coordination among the manager, coach, doctor, psychologist and players.

Unit-III
1. Teaching of volleyball skills.
2. Preparing a lesson plan.
3. Specific training methods for different playing positions.
4. Counselling during competitions.
5. Information and publicity of the competition, writing press release and reports.
6. Facility management, quality control of equipment and player's kit, risk management, medical check-up, medical aid and insurance.
7. Personnel management and interpersonal communication skills.

Unit-IV
1. Injuries associated with the game: Ankle sprain, finger injuries, shoulder dislocation, knee displacement.
2. Preventive and safety measures, P.R.I.C.E., Rehabilitation and physiotherapy.
3. Training means for development of different components of physical fitness i.e. Speed, Strength, Endurance, Flexibility, Coordinative ability.

PRACTICAL COURSE

Course Code: PED302PR – Specialization in Football

Unit-I
1. History of game, measurement and preparation of the play field and equipment required for game.
2. Fundamental skills and lead-up games.
3. Techniques, strategies and method of play.
4. Rules and regulations of the game.
5. National and International tournaments associated with the game.

6. Team/Individual records (World, Olympic, Asian and National Level) of the game.
7. Awards associated with the game.
8. Duties of the officials.
9. Technical Equipment for officiating.
10. Knowledge of the score sheets.
11. Signals of officiating.

Unit-II
1. General and specific warming-up and cooling down.
2. Long-term and short-term preparation for the decisive football competitions.
3. Psychological qualities and preparation of a football player.
4. Offensive, defense system in play, service and reception pattern.
5. Individual, group and team tactics.
6. Diet and nutrition for a football player.
7. Coordination among the manager, coach, doctor, psychologist and players.

Unit-III
1. Teaching of football skills.
2. Preparing a lesson plan.
3. Specific training methods for different playing positions.
4. Counselling during competitions.
5. Information and publicity of the competition, writing press release and reports.
6. Facility management, quality control of equipment and player's kit, risk management, medical check-up, medical aid and insurance.
7. Personnel management and interpersonal communication skills.

Unit-IV
1. Injuries associated with the game: Ankle sprain, finger injuries, shoulder dislocation, knee displacement.
2. Preventive and safety measures, P.R.I.C.E., Rehabilitation and physiotherapy.
3. Training means for development of different components of physical fitness i.e. Speed, Strength, Endurance, Flexibility, Coordinative ability.

PRACTICAL COURSE

Course Code: PED303PR – Specialization in Kabaddi

Unit-I

1. History of game, measurement and preparation of the play field and equipment required for game.
2. Fundamental skills and lead-up games.
3. Techniques, strategies and method of play.
4. Rules and regulations of the game.
5. National and International tournaments associated with the game.
6. Team/Individual records (World, Olympic, Asian and National Level) of the game.
7. Awards associated with the game.
8. Duties of the officials.
9. Technical Equipment for officiating.
10. Knowledge of the score sheets.
11. Signals of officiating.

Unit-II

1. General and specific warming-up and cooling down.
2. Long-term and short-term preparation for the decisive kabaddi competitions.
3. Psychological qualities and preparation of a kabaddi player.
4. Offensive, defense system in play, service and reception pattern.
5. Individual, group and team tactics.
6. Diet and nutrition for a kabaddi player.
7. Coordination among the manager, coach, doctor, psychologist and players.

Unit-III

1. Teaching of kabaddi skills.
2. Preparing a lesson plan.
3. Specific training methods for different playing positions.
4. Counselling during competitions.
5. Information and publicity of the competition, writing press release and reports.
6. Facility management, quality control of equipment and player's kit, risk management, medical check-up, medical aid and insurance.

7. Personnel management and interpersonal communication skills.

Unit-IV

1. Injuries associated with the game: Ankle sprain, finger injuries, shoulder dislocation, knee displacement.
2. Preventive and safety measures, P.R.I.C.E., Rehabilitation and physiotherapy.
3. Training means for development of different components of physical fitness i.e. Speed, Strength, Endurance, Flexibility, Coordinative ability.

PRACTICAL COURSE

Course Code: PED304PR – Specialization in Athletics

Unit-I

1. Introduction to athletics.
2. Historical developmental of athletics, Ancient Olympics and Modern Olympics games.
3. Historical review of track and field with special reference to India.
4. National and International level athletics championships: Olympic Games, Asian games, IAAF-World Championship, Commonwealth Games, National Games, Open National, Youth National and Inter-Universities athletics championships.

Unit-II

1. Athletic track and its types.
2. Procedure and methods to mark the track (200m, 400m).
3. Marking and construction of Shot Put, Discus Throw, Javelin throw and Hammer throw arena.
4. Specification and construction of Long Jump, Triple Jump high jump and pole vault pit/runways etc.
5. Selected National and International personalities in athletics.
6. Need, importance and procedure of Warming-up and Cooling down.
7. First aid and rehabilitation of athletics injuries.

Unit-III

1. Track Events: Brief background, technique, training and important motor components of the following track events:

i) Sprints races: 100m, 200m, 400m; Hurdle Races: High Hurdle and Low Hurdle and Steeple Chase.
ii) Middle and Long Distance Races; Combined Events: Decathlon and Hepthalon; Relay Races and Marathon.

2. Fields Events: Brief background, technique, training and important motor components of the following field events:
i) Shot put, Discus throw, Javelin throw and Hammer Throw.
ii) Long Jump, Triple Jump, High Jump and Pole vault.

Unit-IV
1. Technical training and practice of following events:
i) Sprints Starting techniques, finishing techniques.
ii) Shot put, Discus throw and Javelin throw (Basic Teaching Stages)
iii) Long Jump, Triple Jump High Jump and Pole vault (Basic Teaching Stages)
iv) Record files, calculations of straight, radius and staggers of standard tracks.
v) Relays: Holding of the baton and various types of baton exchange (visual and non-visual).

Theory Course

Course Code: PED305TH

Recreation

UNIT-I

Introduction

Meaning of Recreation

Recreation refers to all those activities that people choose to refresh their body and mind and make their leisure time more interesting and enjoyable. Walking, swimming, meditating, reading, playing sports and dancing are examples of recreational activities. Recreation plays an important role in physical education because all the events of physical education depend on Recreation, in Recreation a player prepares himself for a particular event before starting any event. In Recreation, people learn about an event in an entertaining way. Recreation is an essential part of human life and finds many different forms that are naturally shaped by individual interests but also by the surrounding social constructs. Recreation provides many students with a sense of fun and enjoyment inside and outside of school. Recreation challenges students to expand their horizons, prove themselves, and develop new skills and abilities. Many recreational activities require that students take risks and step outside their comfort zone. Certain types of Recreation encourage students to express themselves, learn more about themselves, and connect more deeply with others. Recreation has different meanings to different individuals and is applied to a variety of activities. Sometimes the term is applied to activities of young people and adults to distinguish those activities from young children's play. Due to this diversity in the usage of the term it is desirable to understand clearly in the beginning to avoid confusion. In common usage, however, Recreation has a much broader meaning and is not limited to any particular age group and activity. Research has shown that recreation is an important factor in the quality of life for everyone, including people with disabilities. People who engage in recreational activities will benefit from improved cardiovascular function, better ability to sleep, better self-esteem, increased stamina, and decreased stress levels, all of which not only improve quality of life. But there are positive benefits for other activities as well. Leisure can also be seen as activities people engage in in their free time that are not work oriented or that do not involve life maintenance tasks such as house cleaning or sleeping. Leisure as an activity encompasses activities we engage in for reasons as diverse as relaxation, competition or development and may include reading for pleasure, meditating, painting and participating in sports. Recreation is life itself designed to regain lost energy and attain a sense of enjoyment, freshness, satisfaction and accomplishment. In the modern era, pressure to perform is prominently visible in all age groups, be it children in schools, youth in colleges, adults at work place, everyone wants to shine and be a step ahead of the peers. This constant need among individuals to survive in this demanding environment leaves them exhausted and socially incapable of having truly healthy inter-personal relationships.

Recreation is any activity that people choose to do during their leisure or free time for fun, enjoyment, or satisfaction. Recreation is known as a function of diversion: an activity that distracts, entertains, refreshes, or stimulates the mind, body, and spirit. It is an activity that renews your health and spirits through pleasure and relaxation. Recreation refreshes a person's strength and soul after work. The use of leisure time to satisfy desires such as recreation, amusement, sports, adventure, or education. To satisfy these desires, those who have the time to participate in them and the means to pay for them seek out an ever-increasing variety of experiences. Exercise causes the body to perform a physical activity that results in a healthy or healthy level of physical fitness and mental health. In other words, the purpose of exercise is to maintain or increase our physical fitness and general health. Recreation are activities, pastimes, and experiences that are freely chosen.

They are usually done in free time and create a feeling of well-being, fulfilment, joy, relaxation and satisfaction. Leisure refers to the free time that people can spend away from their everyday responsibilities (such as work and household tasks) to rest, relax and enjoy life. It is during leisure time that people participate in recreational and sporting activities. Leisure is the concept of free time that each of us has. Time when we are not working or have other obligations because it allows us to rest and recharge. Therefore, we can participate in leisure activities such as relaxing, enjoying our hobbies, or spending time with family and friends in our free time. Some leisure activities include reading, watching TV, going for walks, and spending time with family and friends. According to Richard Cross, Recreation involves an activity or experience that is usually chosen voluntarily by the participant, either because of the immediate gratification he derives from it, or because he expects some personal or social benefit from it. Recognizes values. It is done in leisure time, and has no work meaning, such as studying for a job promotion.

Aims and Objectives of Recreation

- Recreational sports empower people by influencing their self-confidence and self-esteem.

- All people should have the opportunity to live and enjoy nature and cultural landscapes where people's different needs are met. High access areas are defined, known and appreciated, and managed with a long-term view.

- Access to nature for outdoor recreation aims to ensure that spatial planning and land use consider the need for access to attractive nature and cultural landscapes for outdoor recreation.

- The aim of good knowledge about outdoor recreation should be established research and statistical collection on outdoor recreation. It should be based on its broad scope and multidisciplinary nature, have a long-term approach and be based on the diverse needs of outdoor recreation stakeholders. Public authorities, municipalities, landowners, companies and civil society organizations should be well acquainted with and have knowledge in matters related to outdoor recreation, spatial planning, sustainable resource use, and nature and cultural tourism.

- Recreational activities give you the opportunity to be with your loved ones. Going out with your family or going on a picnic with close friends not only refreshes your mind and body but also your relationship with your loved ones.

- Fun activities that involve risk and adventure help you develop self-confidence. Like trekking and camping they train you to face adverse conditions. Adventure sports help in building a courageous attitude. Involvement in sports helps you develop team spirit. Recreation in the form of group activities or team games helps build teamwork and also develops planning and organizing skills. Such activities also help in enhancing interpersonal skills.

- Maintain, develop and modify facilities to increase accessibility for people of all abilities.

- Recreation is important because it allows you to break away from your daily routine and gives you a chance to do what you love. The top purposes of Recreation include enjoyment, socialization and development of your personality.

- Recreation provides many students with a sense of fun and enjoyment inside and outside of school. Recreation challenges students to expand their horizons, prove themselves, and develop new skills and abilities.

- Many recreational activities require that students take risks and step outside their comfort zone.

- Certain types of Recreation encourage students to express themselves, learn more about themselves, and connect more deeply with others.

- Recreation can give students a sense of self satisfaction, accomplishment and pride that can carry over into other areas and fields.

Physical Education and Recreation

Recreation has a vital role in physical education as all physical activities rely on it. It allows athletes to mentally prepare for specific events and helps individuals learn new activities in a fun and enjoyable manner. Recreation is an integral part of human life, taking various forms based on personal interests and societal influences. Recreational activities can be done alone or with others, involve physical exertion or relaxation, take place indoors or outdoors, have positive or negative effects on health, and contribute to society or have negative impacts. Many recreational activities are considered hobbies, providing regular enjoyment and pleasure.

Engaging in recreational activities helps us combat fatigue, reenergize ourselves, and experience happiness. Without recreation, life would lack excitement and joy. Leisure is the precious time that individuals have for themselves, allowing them the freedom to pursue their interests. It is essential to be knowledgeable about making productive use of leisure time. Recreation refers to the leisure activities that individuals choose to enhance their well-being and overall quality of life. These activities are constructive and beneficial for our physical, mental, and social health.

Need and Importance of Recreation in Modern Age

- Recreation consists of activities or experiences undertaken during leisure, usually voluntarily chosen by the participant either because of satisfaction, enjoyment or creative enrichment, or because he or she perceives some personal or social value to be derived from them. Is. It can also be thought of as a process of participation, or as an emotional state derived from participation.

- It helps in communication skills and team building as students have to work in groups to solve problems. There will be more discussion of ideas and reactions and help students resolve conflicts among themselves. It also helps to enhance memory because there is more practical experience and information can be more fully absorbed by the brain in a more fresh and attractive environment.

- It also helps with moral development because students have the opportunity to take leadership, question actions and rules, and accept responsibility for their own behavior.

- It is recommended to make adventure activities a part of Recreation. Studies have shown that participating in adventure activities has a positive impact on life. Adventure inspires you, boosts your confidence and increases self-awareness. Recreation often includes physical activities such as hiking, bicycling, fishing, and outdoor sports. These activities make you feel refreshed and relaxed. The excitement and thrill that comes with adventure sports adds to the freshness. Sports make you feel challenged, encourage you to take risks, showcase your skills, thus building self-confidence.

- Recreational activities can also be physical activities. To lift weights, you can go to the gym, run, and cycle, do stretching or do yoga or Pilate's exercises at home. All these activities are beneficial for your health. If you do these daily or every other day then you can remain healthy. Doing something you love, which is a recreational activity, is also good for the body on a hormonal level.

- Recreational activities, especially outdoor activities improve one's health such as maintaining a low body fat percentage, reducing blood and cholesterol levels, increasing muscle strength, flexibility, muscular endurance, body composition and Cardiovascular endurance. Overall it increases one's stamina and energy levels resulting in more focus on academic activities, while also impacting one's class attendance and attention leading to more learning.

- Recreation, especially in nature, helps to relax our minds and stimulate us cognitively, resulting in greater productivity at work. Our brains also release more serotonin, a happiness hormone, which improves our mood, relieves stress, and makes us better co-workers, friends, and family members. Additionally, recreation programs in a community can drive overall health outcomes, improve quality of life, and promote greater inclusion by allowing us to get to know neighbours who are from different cultures or non-threatening. Have different viewpoints in the environment.

- It helps in balancing the academic workload with the help of a better physical as well as mental stature of the mind. Recreation serves as a tool that helps a person improve their personality, improve their physical stature, and reduce stress and anxiety, while contributing to better creative expansion.

- Making friends may be difficult for some children. Recreation provides a common activity that can start friendships and maintain them through a shared interest or hobby. Try to see every recreational activity as an opportunity to meet a new friend and become someone else's new friend.

- Children who are blind or have low vision should be treated like their peers. They are just as capable and expecting them to participate in recreational activities will boost their self-esteem. If they are told they "can" instead of "can't", they will expect more of themselves. Through every accomplishment, their self-esteem will improve, leading to greater independence.

- Participation in recreation programs and activities has the potential to facilitate the development of personal abilities, attitudes and beliefs that support inclusion. This is due to the cooperative nature of many recreational activities. For example, being part of a team helps people learn about "teamwork" and cooperation.

- Participating in sports and Recreation provides opportunities to connect with people from different backgrounds that we might not otherwise be able to meet. The casual environment of games helps foster new friendships just by showing up to play. Being part of a community also helps provide accountability. Adults are used to sticking to project deadlines and meetings, but often allow other tasks to take over workout time.

Arrangement of Recreation Centres

The Delhi government's recreation centres aim to provide an ideal haven for senior citizens, offering them a vibrant environment to spend time with friends and peers. A recreation facility (indoor) means a building or place used predominantly for indoor recreation, whether or not operated for the purposes of gain, including a squash court, indoor swimming pool, gymnasium, table tennis centre, health studio, bowling alley, ice rink or any other building or place of a like character used for indoor recreation. Recreation centers are crucial for helping youth develop lifelong healthy habits. Kids and teens can use recreation centers to explore new sports, get free training in using exercise equipment, and form connections with their gym-going peers. The social benefits radiate out into all parts of youths' lives participating in leagues, afterschool programs, and camps at recreation centers helps them solidify their teamwork and leadership. Recreation centers are lifelines for many families. Their programming often includes family-oriented programs, meaning everything from kid-and-parent fitness classes, picnics, and festivals. Plus, there's childcare. That part can't be emphasized strongly enough, cause low-cost childminding is beyond rare. That support makes it possible for parents to participate in community activities and take much-needed breathers. Recreation centres offer a wide range of activities. These may include craft, vocational or educational training classes and services; counselling and professional services; sports facilities such as a gym, swimming pool, tennis or racquetball courts, or weightlifting rooms; or lodging or boarding facilities. Recreation centers are major contributors to local economies. They're a source of jobs ranging from administration and to fitness leadership, and many trainers get their start supporting clients in community centers.

UNIT-II

Camping

Concept and Meaning of Camp

Camping is an outdoor activity involving overnight stays away from home in a shelter, such as a tent or a recreational vehicle. Typically participants leave developed areas to spend time outdoors in more natural ones in pursuit of activities providing them enjoyment. Camping provides a host of benefits. Simply put, camping is good for you, both in body and mind. Benefits include relationship building, opportunities to learn and develop new skills, unplugging and getting away from screens, connecting with nature, stress reduction, and increasing physical fitness. Camping is a key part of many youth organizations around the world, such as Scouting, which use it to teach both self-reliance and teamwork. Camping and spending time in the great outdoors has many benefits from enjoying activities in a clean and healthy environment to learning new skills and reducing anxiety and stress.

Aims and Objectives of Camp

Camping has a common purpose of being a recreational and educational activity. The purpose of camping is to develop the camper, develop his/her relationship with the natural environment, develop personal aspirations, psychological behavior and social skills; Provide opportunities to be independent thus developing their decision making abilities and practicing self-discipline; Develop team spirit and develop leadership skills.

- To expand the recreational and educational benefits of outdoor life.
- To emphasize spiritual opportunities through the camp.
- Providing more opportunities to develop fellowship among campers.
- To encourage high professional/academic standards of camp leadership.
- To gain educational, recreational and social experiences in outdoor life away from home.

- To provide opportunities to meet and learn from other people by living together and participating together in the camping experience.
- To provide opportunities for young people to learn to take responsibility for their own decisions and actions.
- Seeking out and providing opportunities to develop leadership skills.
- To discover special talents among campers and teen leaders and to provide opportunities to develop these talents.
- Learning to fulfil individual and collective responsibilities.
- To provide for the exchange of experiences and successful practices and the development of materials, standards and other assistance for the advancement of camping.

Types of Camp

Car Camping

Car camping is really convenient. It's hard to argue with the ease of driving to your campsite with everything you need in your trunk or truck bed. Car camping is an alternative to Recreational Vehicle camping. It can literally mean camping or sleeping in your car. However, when you dig in a little further, it also means sleeping in a tent or backpack after packing all your camping gear in your car and driving it to a campsite. While car camping has two different meanings, depending on which path you choose, you may need different types of equipment. You also need to find a different place to sleep. Car camping consists of putting your camping gear into your car and heading to a campsite that allows you to park your car and set up your car with a specially designed tent or set up a separate tent nearby. Car camping (also known as drive-up camping) is described as it sounds: Rather than backpacking and pitching a tent, hauling a camper, or bunking up in a cabin, campers can drive up to the campsite and choose to either sleep directly in their vehicle, or set up camp and use the car as storage. Car camping is any type of camping where you can drive your vehicle into your campsite. Car camping allows you to pack in more gear and heavier gear than you would if you were backpacking or canoe camping. Both of which require you to carry all your gear over many miles of terrain.

Bicycle Touring Camping

Bicycle touring can be as simple as a weekend jaunt or as monumental as an around-the-world adventure. Either approach offers a healthy and rewarding way to explore. Combining cycling with camping is my favourite way to spend time outdoors. Getting out bicycle camping on your own is just the start. Heading out with friends, family and larger groups adds a whole other level of fulfilment to the adventure.

Kayak Camping

Kayak camping is a unique adventure. It gives you the best of camping and kayaking, giving you days at a time on the water, uninterrupted by the stresses of everyday life. You can catch your dinner on the water, park at your campsite, and enjoy it before spending the night under the stars. Kayak camping refers to taking all your camping gear in your kayak, to camp on the bank on river or lake paddling trips. Kayak camping is wonderful. During the day you can paddle and use the breaks for fishing. In the evening the tent is set up at the camping site, a delicious dinner is prepared and the late evening hours are spent comfortably in front of a campfire. Simply put, kayak camping is a type of outdoor recreational activity (and, to some extent, a sport) where you travel from site to site over several days, using the kayak as your primary source of transportation between each location. While you're kayak camping, you'll be sleeping in campsites on land. No matter how sleepy or tired you might get while paddling, it's not a good idea to sleep in your kayak for reasons discussed below.

RV & Van Camping

Camping in a van is relatively simple, but you need to have the right van to do so. Instead of needing a lot of extra tent gear and accessories, you can have all of your equipment together in your van. You can camp out of a van with a bed, food, and proper ventilation. However, most people prefer to make it a bit more like home, including all sorts of fun designs and additions. Van camping is quite literally the act of camping in a van. People modify the inside of their vans to have the modern amenities that they need everywhere they go.

Tent Camping

Tent camping is a perfect option for families with children as it creates the chance to bond and learn how to work together. Tent camping is a form of outdoor recreation in which people sleep outdoors in the shelter of a tent. There are a number of variations on tent camping, ranging from erecting a tent in the backyard over the summer to snow camping, in which campers are equipped with specialized gear so that they can safely camp. Tent camping is an easy getaway. It doesn't have to be complicated, and you can do it just about anywhere you can tote and pitch a tent. From backpacking trips to beach camping, the opportunities for tent camping are just about limitless. This involves heading to a park where you can pitch your tent where you will sleep for some nights. You can go tent camping on a campsite, a beach, in the woods, or anywhere you like. Tent camping is a great option to try out for people that are new to camping and wants to start without having to spend a lot of money.

Backpacking Camping

Backpacking means everything you need on your adventure is in a pack on your back. That includes clothes, food, personals and of course camping gear. Backpacking also means that there is at least one overnight in the plan, but can stretch to days or even weeks. Backpacking trips range from short one-night trips to multi-day trips. Some trips start at one trailhead and end at another. And some backpackers even set out on months-long distance end-to-end treks called thru-hikes. Backpacking adventures rarely follow local trails and are more off-the-beaten-path. Pre-planning is a must; knowing the route and camping location before the leaving makes the experience much more enjoyable. Backpacking is an adventure that blends hiking with backcountry camping. It lets you broaden your horizons beyond the car campground to enjoy a richer, more immersive outdoor experience. A backpacking trip can range from night to several months. Backpacking trip gives you the chance to spend time away from the hustle and bustle of everyday life while you get closer to nature. Backpacking is very cost-friendly, and you can experience the great outdoors in ways that most people will never experience.

Glamping

Glamping offers the same exposure to the great outdoors as traditional camping, but the amenities found at the campsite and in the tents themselves far exceed anything most campers have ever experienced. Glamping, a combination of glamorous stays and camping ways, offers its guests with the best of both worlds. This includes luxurious accommodations for comfort in the midst of nature to achieve relaxation and serenity, and of course, a whole lot of memories. Glamping accommodations can include anything from beautiful canvas tents to giant treehouses and more, and there are glamping destinations all over the world! Here's everything you need to know about this stylish camping trend, its origins, and how you can start planning your next glamping getaway. Glamping really is for everyone. Whether you're a couple needing a relaxing retreat away surrounded by nature, a family wanting all the fun of the great outdoors without the stress and the hassle of traditional camping or a group of friends wanting to get together, whilst still having your own space.

Survivalist Camping

Survival camping (also known as survivalist camping) involves living for multiple days (or weeks) in the wilderness, relying upon survival skills and minimal camping gear. This form of rugged outdoor recreation requires far more advanced outdoor survival skills than the casual camper may possess (like foraging for food and navigating from deep in the woods). Survivalist camping is for people looking to put their skills and abilities, both physically and mentally, to the ultimate test. It involves walking into or being dropped off in unknown territory with very limited resources to use for surviving. Survivalist camping requires many skills. The most important of these skills may be finding and purifying water. While many humans can survive a few weeks without food, water is a need that people can't ignore. Even with minimal or no supplies, it is possible to filter water in the wilderness. In this type of camping, you will need to learn all the skills that you will need to survive in a variety of outdoor situations. In survivalist camping, you are going to hunt for food in the wild and also discover emergency medical treatments by yourself. By acquiring these skills, you will be able to survive in case of emergency or during harsh weather conditions.

Ultralight Camping

Ultralight camping is camping with a very light base weight load and takes place on backpacking trips where you're hiking or running with your pack as opposed to car camping where you can load up with your best double burner camping stove and family sized tent. Your base weight is the total weight of all your camping gear excluding items like food, water and fuel that you will consume or use along the way. The lightweight backpacking approach refines the essentials, embraces a true "less is more" attitude, and eliminates weight at every opportunity, aiming for a base weight of 20 pounds or below. The idea is that a hiker carrying less weight can travel farther, faster, while expending less energy.

Winter Camping

Winter camping is camping which takes place in winter weather; most people are talking specifically about snow camping when they mention winter camping, although it can also refer more generally to camping in cooler conditions. There are a number of reasons to go winter camping, and many people find it quite enjoyable, especially if they are already experienced hikers, backpackers, or campers. Just like warm-weather camping, there is a huge range of winter-camping experiences that people from novices to extreme athletes can try from testing the waters with backyard or car camping to luxury guided tours to extended backcountry adventures requiring skis or snowshoes.

Hammock Camping

Hammock camping lets you sleep close to nature and is suitable for many different environments. The ease and versatility of hammock camping have made it a favourite for backpackers, day hikers and even campground campers. One of the benefits of hammock camping is that the curve of the fabric provides a natural and comfortable sleeping position so you'll get a solid night's rest. Some hammocks come with zipped covers, so you can partially zip your hammock to provide added warmth and protection while you rest. Hammock camping is a style of camping that involves sleeping in a hammock suspended above the ground instead of in a tent, or another type of campsite lodging. Hammocks tend to be much lighter than tents and are also easier and faster to set-up. A hammock will generally weigh a lot less than even the best camping tents. It will also take up a lot less room. Based on that alone, if hammock camping works, it is a far superior option compared to bringing a bulky tent. Hammock camping simply means you're swapping out your typical tent in favour of a hammock and a few helpful accessories where you can comfortably sleep outdoors overnight. Many backpackers and bike backers enjoy camping with hammocks because they are so lightweight and take up little space in a pack. Hammock campers also enjoy a higher vantage point and are spared the discomfort of sleeping on sloped or rocky ground. A couple of sturdy trees are all you need.

Backyard Camping

Backyard camping is simple and doesn't require a lot of preparation or equipment. A tent and sleeping bag is really all that is needed, but other items will enhance the experience. Blankets can replace a sleeping bag. One of the best parts of backyard camping is that it's so easy to build a "campfire" if you have a built-in fire pit as part of your yard's hardscape or a portable one! Although the fire can be a dangerous place for young kids, help them learn about fire safety before your big camp out and get them involved by making fire starters. Sleeping under the stars is an awesome experience, but too often mosquitos will necessitate the use of a tent. Other items make a backyard campout more enjoyable such as a flashlight, pillow, and ground pad and insect repellent. Too many items take away the simplicity and add clutter. Keep it simple.

Bivy Sack Camping

Bivy sacks are single-person, minimalist shelters that offer an additional layer of protection against the environment for you and your sleeping bag think cowboy camping with a full-body shell. A bivy sack is a small, simple and extremely lightweight sack for your best sleeping bag and is used in place of a tent. The word "bivy" is short for the French word "bivouac" which evolved to refer to a temporary camp without tents or shelter, used mostly by soldiers and mountaineers. A basic bivy sack essentially just looks like a nylon slipcover for your sleeping bag and sleeping pad that has a waterproof layer made from a breathable fabric like Gore-Tex and a drawstring opening for your head, so you can sleep inside it instead of a tent. A wide variety of bivy sack designs exist for camping in different conditions. You can choose between waterproof and non-waterproof breathable options. Some bivies zip completely closed to keep insects and water out. Some bivies use a small pole to keep the material off of your face as you sleep. Basic bivies and emergency bivies simply leave the face open.

Tarp Camping

The purpose of the tarp is for protection from wind and rain while you sleep. Tarps come in three main types: flat, shaped and tarp-tents.

Flat tarps, which are square or rectangular, are the simplest option. Shaped tarps are multi-sided (i.e. heptagonal or hexagonal) or have curved edges, with the shape specifically designed by the manufacturers to enable clever and precise pitching. Tarp-tents, on the other hand, blur the line between tarp and tent, and can be pitched in different ways and often include advanced features such as zips or doors. Camping tarps are durable, waterproof, and versatile pieces of camping gear in outdoor survival scenarios. For example, a hiker can use a tarp as a heavy rain fly or awning over their tent, or they can use it to create a hammock tarp roof. Tarp camping is a minimalist method of shelter construction in which a camper uses a tarpaulin, or tarp to shield their body and equipment from the wind, rain, and other elements. In its simplest form, a camping tarp is simply a rectangular piece of waterproof fabric. You hang the tarp above your body with a series of ropes, poles, and stakes. Tarps don't include a floor, bug netting, or walls.

Agencies Promoting Camp

All India Council of Sports

The council will have the aims and objectives of popularising sports amongst the youth as a way of life, increasing outreach of sports to rural and tribal areas, areas affected by left wing extremism, North East and Jammu & Kashmir, implementation of policies for promotion of sports and games in the country, matters relating to promotion of inclusiveness in sports with special focus on women, differently-abled, tribals etc, preventing drug abuse in sports, fraud in age and sexual harassment of women in sports, among others. Council will meet and deliberate on matters pertaining to the promotion and development of athletics and sports in India. The Council will also engage in policy implementation for generating interest for sports and games in the nation. The Council is also involved in the promotion of inclusiveness in sports with a focus on differently abled, those with special needs and more. The council will meet from time to time, at least once in a quarter, and deliberate on matters relating to the promotion and development of sports and games in the country.

International Olympic Committee

The International Olympic Committee is the guardian of the Olympic Games and the leader of the Olympic Movement. The vision of the International Olympic Committee is to build a Better World through Sport.

Role

1. To encourage and support the organisation, development and coordination of sport and sports competitions.
2. To ensure the regular celebration of the Olympic Games.
3. To act against any form of discrimination affecting the Olympic Movement.
4. To encourage and support the promotion of women in sport at all levels.

The International Olympic Committee (IOC) is a not-for-profit independent international organisation that is committed to building a better world through sport. Created on 23 June 1894, just under two years before the first Olympic Games of the modern era in April 1896, the IOC is the supreme authority of the Olympic Movement. A truly global organisation, it acts as a catalyst for collaboration between all Olympic stakeholders, including the athletes, the National Olympic Committees, the International Federations, Organising Committees for the Olympic Games, the Worldwide Olympic Partners and Olympic broadcast partners. It also collaborates with public and private authorities including the United Nations and other international organisations.

Young Women Christian Association

The Young Women Christian Association is a Christian, membership, nonpartisan, non-governmental organization (NGO) dedicated to the empowerment of the community, especially women, youth and children, to realize their potential as human beings and to contribute to a just society, through rights based and sustainable interventions. The YWCA of India supports work at the community level, and also seeks to change broader systems, including weak government policy and enforcement, providing vocational skills training for women for economic empowerment, educational opportunities for children and eradicating harmful social norms.

Educative Value of Camp

Camping is a great way to learn self-sufficiency and to hone our ability to survive in the face of disaster or unexpected circumstances. While camping, opportunities often come up for small children to learn fire safety and basic first aid. Older kids can learn how to clean and gut a fish, how to find water that is safe to drink. On school adventure trips, students get various opportunities to excel in several social skills, from developing new relationships to strengthening old bonds. Some activities focusing on these areas include tidying up their own cabins, team building exercises, helping with meal preparations and overcoming personal challenges, such as cycling, trekking, giant swing etc. Since your children will always have to eat, don't overlook teaching them these important life skills. When we go on a camping trip, we work very hard to make sure that we've carefully planned meals so we don't have to leave the state park during our long weekend there. Children might attend an educational camping experience that focuses on musical theatre or wilderness skills for a few weeks, or they could attend something broader. Camping is the ideal time for family bonding. Away from work, school, errands, and other routine responsibilities, we have the opportunity to simply enjoy each other's company.

UNIT-III

Recreational Activities

Types of Recreation

Rural Recreation

Recreational activities in rural communities are not only simple but also limited. The nature and type of recreational activities in a village depend on its economic and social progress. Rural recreational opportunities are enhanced, including horseback riding facilities, trails, and more. Commercial type recreational activities are not found in villages. But recreation growth comes with potential problems. Some of the problems are related to development such as congested roads, overcrowded schools, environmental stress, housing shortage, degraded landscapes, and conflicts over land use and public policies. Rural communities are often characterized by less access to infrastructure and resources to engage in physical activity compared to urban centres. Rural schools are limited by environmental constraints, particularly the lack of verification of physical education resources. Therefore, improving the allocation and utilization efficiency of rural physical education resources is an important element of rural physical education construction. Physical education is an important physical basis for the current development of students, as well as for their future work and life, and without a healthy body it is impossible to have a bright future. Agriculture sector is the driving force of India. A large number of Indian population is involved in the business of agriculture and allied industries. Similarly, there are many sectors arising from the rural society that drive the economy. With education, rural populations can apply new knowledge and better techniques and practices to their businesses. The reason for low literacy rate in rural areas in India is the lack of awareness about the importance of education. People in rural areas are mostly engaged in agriculture and allied sectors. Children are engaged in these areas from the very beginning and do not give much importance to their studies. Rural schools tend to harbor untrained or unqualified teachers. School inspectors do not like walking or riding in canoes for several days, so remote schools are rarely visited.

Urban Recreation

Urban recreational spaces are becoming more and more experimental and unique and more and more defined in terms of functionality, aesthetics and identity. Students will participate in activities such as skateboarding, walking, bike riding, aquatics while using the community facilities. This elective enables students to develop self-esteem, social skills, and teamwork and group skills. Students will also investigate local recreational facilities and study community use and environmental impact. Students will work in groups to plan and develop a new recreation facility for the local community. Urban education is a method of schooling that takes place in large, densely populated areas with diverse populations. It may refer to the conditions and demands that characterize teaching and learning in large metropolitan areas. Schools that provide urban education experiences typically have high enrollment rates and a complex bureaucratic system. The term urban education means providing knowledge in a densely populated area. The population may be of diverse cultures, religions and ethnicities. It is the schooling of large numbers of students with diverse learning strategies. Urban education involves a high rate of enrolment. It puts cooperative learning theory into practice. With the establishment of a proper learning, education involves a particular method of instruction. Academics focus on the characteristics of urban challenges. Like culture and the arts, entertainment, leisure and sporting activities play an important role in communities. Their many benefits include improving the health and well-being of individuals, contributing to the empowerment of individuals, and promoting the development of inclusive communities. Recreation, leisure and sporting activities can involve individuals, small groups, teams or entire communities and are relevant to people of all different ages, abilities and skill levels.

Industrial Recreation

Recreation through sports provides opportunity for socialization, encouragement, cooperation which creates a kind of strength and self-confidence in the individual. The recreation and leisure industry is defined as work that enhances well-being through providing and facilitating services and programs, leading personnel and operations, and allocating organization resources. The arts and recreation sector includes a wide range of establishments that operate facilities or provide services to cater to the various cultural, and recreational interests of their patrons.

Nature of Recreation

Nature and Outdoor Activities

Outdoor recreation is an organized activity undertaken in one's spare time for personal reasons, where an interaction exists between humans and elements of nature. The many outdoor nature activities for children included here are also helpful for the Nature School Preschool and Forest School Kindergarten. Suggestions include nature study ideas, outdoor science ideas, and nature crafts for toddlers, preschoolers, kindergarteners, elementary school-age children, tweens, and teens. The beauty of getting back to nature and enjoying the wonderful outdoors is that it allows you to switch off all distractions and is therefore the perfect antidote to a busy lifestyle.

Drama Activities

Drama games are essentially activities that are built into the theater, but as you move beyond the realm of acting, these games can help students develop a myriad of skills that come in handy during their learning.

Art and Craft

Art has been described as an unstructured and open-ended form of work; which expresses emotions and vision. Craft refers to a form of work that involves the creation of physical objects using the hands and mind. Art depends on artistic ability whereas craft is based on learned skills and techniques. Art is known to serve an aesthetic purpose. On the other hand, crafts serve human purposes. Art pays special attention to ideas, emotions, and visual qualities. In contrast, craft emphasizes the correct use of tools and materials and the application of technique. Arts and crafts are both forms of visual creativity that are often linked to each other. Many people do not understand the difference between arts and crafts.

Sports

Sport is defined as a human activity that involves physical exertion and skill as the primary focus of the activity, With elements of competition where rules of behavior governing the activity formally exist through organizations and are commonly recognized as a sport. Sports and entertainment can be defined as the vast range of activities that people do in their free time. These include attending sporting and cultural events, participating in sports and physical recreation activities, engaging in hobbies, watching television or videos, listening to music and reading, socializing, and taking vacations.

Dance activities

A dance activity is a planned or facilitated series of movement problems that are solved by the participants. Dancers use their bodies in a variety of ways to move rhythmically or irregularly across space, alone or with others. A dance activity in a school might be learning about different dance styles that are performed in professional settings such as classical ballet, tap, modern dance or hip hop. Dance games are a great way to improve various skills in a child. These games also engage the child physically and mentally. Dance games are fun for everyone who participates. Even the shyest, most hesitant person will get caught up in the excitement and move to the music. In this article, we will share dance games for both kids and teens.

Hobbies and collecting activities

A regular, enjoyable activity done in one's free time is called a hobby. Generally, hobbies are not pursued professionally. Hobbies come in a wide variety and can include physical activities, mental hobbies, and creativity. A hobby is an activity that a person does in his spare time for pleasure, personal satisfaction and relaxation. It is something they do for their own sake rather than for work, academic or financial reasons. Hobbies can range from active activities like sports and fitness, creative activities like painting and writing, intellectual activities like reading and learning new skills, and passive activities like watching movies or listening to music. Hobbies are often either creative or artistic in nature or may be more active such as participating in some type of sport. Hobbies are a great way to be social and meet new friends. Social hobbies facilitate bonding with others and add another layer of support to your life to reduce stress.

Musical Activities

Musical activities such as listening to music, playing an instrument, singing or dancing are also an important source for social interaction, promoting interaction and a sense of belonging with others. Music games for kids are a great way to teach them about different styles of music. Music is definitely relaxing, and many people consider it to be food for the soul. Musical activities are fun, entertaining, and beneficial to our children's cognitive and emotional development. They can make progress in foundational skills in the areas of language, reading, writing, creativity, and mathematics and emotion regulation. Sports are important and music is the best type of sport to get involved in. Music plays a major role in the development of children.

Recreation Providing Agencies

Home

A recreation room is a designated area for various recreational activities. Entertainment rooms, often located away from the main living sections of the home, have long been a popular spot for evenings with friends or classic movie sessions. They are especially useful for teens who like to have fun with friends or who want to be creative without annoying their parents. You can easily convert most of the rooms in the house into an arts and crafts area. Even the smallest spaces can be transformed into rooms where you or your kids can paint and draw without fear of making a mess. If the room will be used for painting, choose a very simple wall material like tile or vinyl. An entertainment room is an important feature in a luxury home, especially when occupied by large families or people who love to entertain. This room is meant to provide entertainment as well as comfort to all its users, irrespective of the age group.

Government

Government entertainment agencies are run by the government and established to provide entertainment facilities to the people. These are federal, state, provincial agencies and local departments that provide recreation and leisure services as a primary function. It also includes other agencies that offer entertainment programs as secondary responsibilities such as those related to social services, education, special populations, and the armed forces. These agencies work to ensure entertainment services to the population without the motive of making money. Government agencies regulate and provide valuable information on entertainment and leisure. Partnerships with city government and city parks and recreation departments provide an opportunity to take cooperative expansion down to the municipal level to work together to support each other's efforts to meet the needs of city residents.

Voluntary

Volunteerism continues to be a very important topic in the field of recreation, sports and parks. Many organizations rely on volunteers for day-to-day operations. They are essential for special sporting and entertainment events such as tournaments and games. Volunteers are becoming more sophisticated. There are also greater demands on volunteers' time. Volunteer management skills are becoming increasingly important for both volunteers and staff working with volunteers. Voluntary organizations also help the state in the area which is its sole responsibility but for which it has limited resources and does such work in a much better way than the state organizations. The voluntary sector is made up of inclusive and exclusive clubs which are non-profit organizations managed essentially by amateur sportsmen and women. The voluntary sector has the largest involvement in sport in the UK, particularly competitive sport. Voluntary sector clubs often work in partnership with the private or public sector, e.g. they use public sector facilities or receive sponsorship from private sector companies. The voluntary sector offers sport for all, starting at a base level of participation. Costs are generally free if not, they are minimal and are paid to cover the cost of facility hire, kit and equipment, with no profits being made from the voluntary organisations. Those who work in this sector do so on a voluntary basis, with a passion for the game and an interest in developing the local game. Access is important, with various voluntary clubs in each local area in accessible locations. Kit and equipment are generally poor due to lack of money, but grants are available to clubs to make improvements each year.

Personal

In this type of recreational agency, entertainment services are provided only to those who are within an institution. Private sector entertainment has recently become a huge industry. Families are spending their holidays traveling to attend their children's sporting events. Spending thousands of dollars on travel, entry fees, equipment and training. Private sports and fitness facilities are emerging. Specialty adventure sports are becoming popular. Boutique yoga and training facilities are on the rise. Leisure, sports and recreation activities play an integral role in the development and improvement of overall community health. Leisure-recreation facilities must meet the needs of the public and all age groups, from children to the elderly population. The sports industry consists of three organizational sectors: public, non-profit, and commercial. These are important categories for a wide variety of organizations involved in sport and are central to the creation and production of sport products, services, programs and facilities.

Commercial Agencies

Commercial recreation means commercial facilities serving the recreational needs of residents and visitors. Current innovations in the commercial entertainment and tourism industry are making activities more enjoyable and tasks more convenient for customers. Technology is a key component of emerging trends in hotels, restaurants and shopping. Mobile apps and streamlined digital shopping have allowed consumers to live fast-paced lives, even at leisure. Commercial recreational uses are sports-oriented facilities that are used for a variety of fitness, recreational or social activities. Activities are primarily by and for the participants; the audience is contingent and exists on a non-recurring basis. Activities may be conducted in an enclosed building or open facilities. Commercial entertainment is the provision of facilities, equipment and programs that meet public demand for activities during non-constrained hours and are profitable for the supplier. The term "commercial entertainment" has been given a negative connotation in the field of entertainment and leisure. Commercial recreational travel enterprises include airlines, rental car services, trains, bus lines, and cruise ships.

Recent Changes in the Recreational Activities

The COVID-19 pandemic has not only resulted in a worldwide health crisis but has also greatly affected the everyday routines of individuals across the globe. Among those significantly impacted are urban outdoor enthusiasts, who are facing numerous challenges due to the pandemic and the subsequent measures put in place by authorities. Stay-at-home orders and recommendations for physical distancing have emerged as potential obstacles for outdoor recreational activities, which are integral to the lifestyles and overall well-being of these enthusiasts. The impact of these restrictions is particularly profound in urban areas, where the limitations on recreational behavior have the greatest consequences.

Responsibilities of a Recreational Manager

The recreational leader has to plan, organize, and coordinate recreational, cultural, and athletic activities for people to enjoy in their leisure time. They work in various institutional set ups such as community centres, municipalities, corporations, clubs and other similar public and private institutions; They are also found in correctional institutions, homes for the elderly, and other facilities that recognize the therapeutic aspects of recreation. A recreation leader is responsible for overseeing sports and other extracurricular activities for nursing homes, youth centers, schools, or parks and recreational departments. The job description for a recreation leader includes the ability to encourage others to work as a team member, as well as promote good sportsmanship and build morale. Entertainment leaders are responsible for the daily operations of an entertainment program. They primarily organize and direct participants, schedule use of facilities, establish records of equipment usage and ensure that recreation facilities and equipment are properly used and maintained. They may lead classes and provide instruction in a recreational activity such as kayaking or golf. One of the main qualities of an entertainment leader is the knowledge and ability to create fun and engaging programs for different categories of individuals. This usually involves understanding the types of activities that specific groups of people are likely to enjoy and finding ways to put them into practice. It also refers to being able to assess the effectiveness of these programs and continuously improve them based on feedback from participants. Courses within the program provide entertainment leaders with skills and knowledge across a wide range of subject areas and enable them to be more effective in the position. Accreditation is also provided for selected courses along with college and entertainment management certificate and diploma programs. Leaders are needed, and are found in all aspects of our daily lives, from the workplace to the schoolyard; And from social clubs to the government. When leadership is good, the chances of getting things done with greater efficiency increase, and there is a higher level of satisfaction among all concerned. Certifications are important for an entertainment leader in the job market because they provide evidence to employers that a person has the skills and knowledge necessary to do the job. Certifications help demonstrate that an entertainment leader has gone through specific training and is qualified to perform certain tasks. They also help employers distinguish between applicants, as those with certifications can show that they have taken extra steps to become more qualified than they would be without them. The Recreation Leader conducts activities with designated groups of all ages in individual programs and at various indoor/outdoor facilities or centers. However good leadership is not something a person is born with. Some personal traits, such as self-confidence, may give some advantages over others; but effective leadership requires more than just a strong personality.

Setting Goals

A leader is expected to do the creative work of formulating goals and policies to persuade subordinates to work with enthusiasm and confidence.

Arrangement

The second function of a leader is to create and shape the organization on a scientific basis by assigning roles suitable to individual capabilities with a view to making its various components operate sensitively towards the achievement of enterprise goals.

Coordination

Leaders have to create cordial relationships between various departments, employees and resources of the organization.

Encourage Teamwork

Team work is always better than individual work. A leader has to develop a sense of team spirit among his followers to perform the given task effectively.

Communications

A leader must communicate with all his followers and let them air their concerns. He should develop a system of two-way communication.

Leader Manages Time Well

Time is precious and important but is often overlooked in management. There are three dimensions of time, time imposed by the boss, time imposed by the system and self-imposed time which are prominent in the literature. Because the leader has knowledge of time management principles such as time preparation charts, scheduling techniques, etc., he is in a position to utilize time productively in organizations.

Safety Knowledge

In addition to finding ways to help different groups of people enjoy themselves, entertainment leaders also ensure the safety of every participant. Knowledge of safety procedures specific to each activity helps recreation leaders plan, create, and manage safe environments.

Event Planning

Entertainment leaders use their specialized knowledge to plan entertaining programs for their clients. This typically involves scheduling the events, determining the appropriate budget to host them, finding the appropriate venue to hold them, hiring personnel to help organize them, and creating a schedule that participants will follow. . Being able to assess participant feedback and continually improve the quality of events is also useful in the role.

Integrity

Integrity is an essential leadership quality for individual and organization. This is especially important for top-level executives who are charting the course of the organization and making countless other important decisions.

Respect

Treating people with respect on a daily basis is one of the most important things a leader can do. This will reduce stress and conflict, build trust and improve effectiveness. Building a culture of respect is more than the absence of disrespect. Respect can be shown in many different ways, but it often starts with being a good listener who genuinely tries to understand others' point of view.

Honesty

One of the essential leadership qualities is the possession of honesty. Honesty is expected from leaders to gain trust and respect from people for credibility. Additionally, we look to people who are true to their word and accountable. Thus, integrity is the most important quality for any business leader or any leader in general.

Responsibility

One of the most important qualities a leader should have is a sense of responsibility and dependability. This means displaying those qualities in your personal work, but also displaying them in your interactions with others. Your team members need to know that they can depend on you to do their fair share of the work and follow through, support them through difficult times, and support them in meeting both shared and individual goals.

Delegate

As a successful leader, you must learn to delegate. Refining your brand, vision and values is essential to building an efficient and nuanced business. But if you don't learn to trust your team to follow your ideas and values, it can be difficult to move forward. Trusting your team with an idea is a sign of strength in leadership.

UNIT-IV
Picnic

Meaning of Picnic

A picnic is a social gathering where people bring food and drinks to share and enjoy in an outdoor setting. It typically involves a casual meal and a relaxed atmosphere, allowing people to spend quality time together in nature.

Picnics are a beloved outdoor activity enjoyed by people of all ages. Picnics have played a significant role in human life for centuries. They allow people to gather and enjoy a meal outdoors, often in a beautiful natural setting. Picnics are one of the most exciting things that children and adults love equally. It helps us divert from daily life and adds a touch of variety to our lives. Moreover, a picnic can take us to another world that is different from the one we live in daily. It adds charm to our life and is a nice refreshment in our life. Picnics are very important as they add pleasantness to our lives. There are different kinds of picnics that people can enjoy. There are family picnics, school picnics, church picnics, union picnics, and more. Picnics make our existence smooth and take us out of our daily routine. Moreover, picnics tend to bring out the best in us. We are able to enjoy physically as well as mentally in picnics.

Importance and Utilities of Picnic

Bond with family and friends
You don't need to go on a fancy vacation or plan an extravagant party to reconnect with family and friends. A simple picnic with a few snacks and light dishes is all you need to have a great time catching up with loved ones. A picnic is a fun and relaxing way to build memories and enjoy the presence of others.

Better behavior
It turns out eating with your kids, such as a picnic lunch, leads to better behavior. Children that eat family meals are less likely to partake in risky behaviors like smoking and drinking. This benefit also translates to academic performance children that eat with their families tend to have higher grades than those who don't. If your child has been testing your limits, try including more family picnics this summer.

Self-reflection time
Parents and children alike can benefit from meditation and self-reflection. Picnics are relatively peaceful environments that encourage these introspective behaviors. It's important to give children time to be alone and learn about themselves through self-reflection, which can easily be done on a picnic.

Personal Development
First and foremost, picnics play a pivotal role in the personal development of students. Outside the classroom's four walls, they learn to be more independent, make decisions, and even develop leadership skills.

Mental Health
Picnics definitely help foster better mental health. Being out in the sun enhances the production of Vitamin D in the body which is extremely important to ward off depression, fatigue and irritability. There is something about playing in the sun that actually brings out our inner happiness. We

feel less restrained & more carefree. Most of us, in our day to day lives (and particularly so in metropolitan cities with its horrors of long work hours, traffic jams and irregular sleep patterns) do not get the time to enjoy the simple joys that life has to offer like breathing in fresh air, enjoying the feeling of the sun on your face, watching the sun rise or set, hearing the birds chirp early in the morning, playing with our pet dog in the park etc.

Social Skills & Team Building

Activities or games can encourage teamwork. Imagine students working together in a scavenger hunt at a botanical garden, deciphering clues, and learning about different plants in the process. They're not just having fun but also honing their team-building and problem-solving skills.

Organization of Picnic

Organization of company picnics is a great idea for integrating employees. Employee picnic is a guarantee of great fun and unforgettable memories. Celebrating outdoors in the company of unique attractions, good food and joyful music will give employees a lot of positive emotions and help them build friendly relationships.

Step 1

Delegate the tasks to guests who will attend the picnic. Get the help of everyone who will be there. Each family can take care of something so the picnic is not the responsibility of one person.

Step 2

Plan ahead. Know who's coming. Find out how many families will attend, what you'll be eating, when you'll get together, where you'll meet and how you'll have fun.

Step 3

Make a list of everything you need. Create a menu which will help you decide what to buy and how much to buy.

Step 4

Decide whether you want hot food like barbeque or cold cuts. Let everyone know what you have decided. Ask about food allergies. Divide your list into items each family can bring.

Step 5
Have a potluck picnic or get one group of people to bring each item. Delegate a group to bring the meat, another can bring the salads or vegetables. Get someone to bring the desserts, another to bring the snacks. Everyone can bring their own drinks.

Step 6
Ask one or two families to buy plastic utensils and paper napkins. You might ask each family to bring chairs, a table cloth and a blanket.

Step 7
Plan activities to keep people busy throughout the day. Choose some family activities and activities for the children. You can plan games and play group sports. Have a craft table set up for the kids.

Step 8
Create a picnic eating area. Keep the food in coolers. Set up picnic tables or picnic blankets and place the coolers nearby. You can keep chips and cut up vegetables on the tables. Pick a time to serve the rest of the food so that everyone can dine together.

Essentials for Picnic

Picnic basket
There's something so satisfying about packing a picnic basket with all your goods, knowing you get to dive into it all later. Having a decent-sized basket to carry your precious cargo is a necessity and if you find one that's stylish as well it makes for a cute decor item on the day.

Picnic Blanket
While some people adore lying on the grass, it is essential to keep food and drink off the dirty ground. If possible, get a waterproof picnic blanket; it's gonna protect you from dump and cold, plus your clothes from dirt as well. A blanket or tablecloth is easy to take along; you can fold it up into your picnic basket. If you prefer not to bring one, make sure you have something else to sit on. Plastic mats or outdoor cushions also work well as they don't get dirty and keep your clothes clean.

Food and drinks

The easiest way to ensure the good times keep rolling is by ensuring you have a decent amount of food and drinks. Consider foods that are easy to prepare and share like a beautifully curated cheeseboard.

Plates & Cutlery

You have a few choices for your plates and cutlery, depending on your preferences and what you're planning to serve. You could bring a nice wooden board for an outdoor charcuterie experience. Some great picnic date ideas that we've seen include using paper plates for the food on the blanket, but providing ceramic mini-plates to actually eat from.

Cooler

A cooler will help keep your perishables and cold food items at the ideal temperature nobody wants to drink lukewarm champagne. If you don't have a cooler, consider bringing a hydro flask or insulated bottle filled with ice to fill glasses with instead.

Vegetable salads

In addition to all the drinks and sandwiches, fruits are another healthy pick for picnics. Fruit salads are a delicious way of ensuring health. There are different food salads like mixed fruit salads, watermelon salads and much more. Making different combinations of fruits of our liking is fun food preparation. Vegetables like lettuce, cucumber, cabbage, carrots etc., are good for making tasty vegetable salads. These salads are extremely healthy, contain various vitamins and are rich in iron. For the person who is conscious about their health, these salads are a great option to take to a picnic.

Factors Affecting Its Organization

Budget

The budget is the first thing you must consider when planning any corporate event. After all, you must pay for entertainment, delicious food, quality venue, drinks, and other catering essentials. Remember that your budget will increase for added guests. So, figure out how much you can afford to spend on your picnic before making significant decisions.

Food

A picnic is primarily a time to eat and drink, so it is worth taking care of a tasty and varied menu that will suit the tastes of the participants. You can organize a barbecue, a buffet with snacks and drinks, as well as a dessert stand with pastries and sweets.

The Right Attractions

Think about what might interest the participants and adjust the attractions to their preferences. These can be outdoor games and fun, competitions, thematic presentations or artistic shows.

Weather

When planning a fun outdoor event, the weather is one of the most critical factors. Try to choose a picnic date when it is unlikely to be rainy or too cold. If you discover a chance of harsh weather ahead of time, postpone the event or start planning for alternative venues.

Pick an attractive local venue

Selecting a new location for your summer picnic each year adds some excitement. Depending on your budget, local park pavilions, amusement or water parks, dinner cruises, outdoor festivals, or even the company premises (if conducive) are all good options for company summer picnic venues.

Atmosphere

Atmosphere is what every event planner strives for, and every company picnic should deliver. The venue plays a large part in establishing atmosphere another reason why the stakes are high to find the perfect company picnic venue. To find the perfect backdrop, have an idea of a company picnic theme (find picnic theme ideas here) before vetting event venues.

Educative Value of Picnic

First and foremost, picnics play a pivotal role in the personal development of students. Outside the classroom's four walls, they learn to be more independent, make decisions, and even develop leadership skills. School picnics should be affordable for all students. Schools need to consider entry fees, transportation, and food costs. School picnics are a cherished part of most students' academic life. It's a time when students get to step outside their usual classroom setting and enjoy some quality time with their friends and teachers in a different environment. This picnic essay tells you how they are a great way of bringing people together. Whether it is your family or your friends, everyone forms a bond at picnics. It is great for emotional bonding. Moreover, it gives us a chance to speak out our minds and unwind and relax. Further, we also get to enjoy physical activities during picnics. The walks and games are beneficial to our body and improve our stamina too.

Recreational and Adventurous Avenues in Himachal Pradesh

For adventurers, it has always been a great and fascinating experience to enjoy thrilling activities in Himachal Pradesh. Hills of Himachal Pradesh hold the feeling of a fairy-tale wonderland, but there's another side to it. The captivating hills can thrill and enthral the groovy backpackers, making Himachal Pradesh a must visit destination for every mountaineer and trekker.

Water Games

Gobind Sagar Lake is a man-made reservoir built in the Bilaspur district. It facilitates many water sport activities in Himachal Pradesh thus appealing to large chunk of tourists to indulge in various such activities like swimming, rowing, water-skiing, surfing, canoeing and kayaking. Rowing and kayaking are usually organized for the experienced campaigners only.

During the summer and autumn season, people can enjoy the best of water sports activities in Himachal Pradesh. Snow and rain-fed rivers of Himachal Pradesh are so cold that it can chill the spines of adventurers. In Himachal Pradesh, water sports activities can be enjoyed in Sutlej, Chenab, and Beas and Ravi River streams.

Paragliding

Paragliding in Himachal Pradesh is a once in a lifetime experience set amidst the backdrop of the stunning Himalayas.

Bir Billing in Himachal Pradesh is one of the most popular spots for paragliding in India. The beautiful mountainous landscape and the cooler climate make it an ideal destination for this adventure sport. There are many operators offering paragliding joyrides in Bir Billing and the prices are quite reasonable. The experience of gliding over the mountains and forests is simply exhilarating and something that you will never forget. Bir Billing is one of the most popular paragliding sites in India and for good reason. The scenery is stunning, with snow-capped mountains and green valleys. The conditions are also great for flying, with strong thermals and good wind conditions.

Winter Games

Himachal Pradesh is a beautiful state is a popular tourist destination for Indians, especially among the newlyweds and youngsters. This is the land of Gods that have been bestowed with snow-capped mountains, fast flowing streams, and valleys, which has a tendency to sink on the ground.

Snow Adventures in Himachal is an absolute delight, full of love and fun. During winter, all the high-altitude places turn white, and they're a sight for sore eyes. Skiing in Himachal is one among other famous adventure sports, drawing tourist sand adventure seekers to the state of Himachal Pradesh. There are two kinds of skiing performed here, one being Alpine kin and the other being Nordic kind. The Alpine kind involves skiing down steeply inclined slopes while the Nordic type is a bit more challenging and comprises jumping and cross country skiing. The Slopes of the Himalayas, including Pir Panjal, Shivalik are ideal for performing this sport.

Mountaineering

The mountain ranges of Dhauladhar, Pir Panjal and Chandra Bhaga in Himachal Pradesh are the best places to enjoy rock climbing and mountaineering in Himachal Pradesh. Some of the prominent rock-climbing sites are Shitidhar Mountain, Friendship Peak in the Pir Panjal Range, Patalsu Peak, Mount Hanuman Tibba, Seven Sisters, Mount Deo Tibba, and Beas Kund. Talking about mountaineering sites Chandratal and Malana glaciers are most popular among ice-climbers.

Manali is one of the most popular destinations when it comes to beginning mountaineering adventures in Himachal Pradesh. The Deo Tibba expedition commences from this town and is one such trip that will give you a thrilling opportunity to experience the sport at its best. It is a challenging expedition and is suitable for those, who have previous trekking and climbing experience. Another expedition, full of incredible sceneries on the way, is the one to Chandratal – a glacial lake.

Trekking

Trekking is one of the most popular activities in Himachal Pradesh. The state is home to some of the country's most scenic and challenging trekking trails. From the high-altitude deserts of Spiti to the lush green forests of

Kullu and Manali, Himachal Pradesh offers a wide range of trekking options that cater to all levels of fitness and experience. Himachal Pradesh is a beautiful destination that offers a unique blend of natural beauty and cultural heritage. The state's trekking trails are a great way to explore its stunning landscape and experience its rich culture.

Himachal Treks

- Bhrigu Lake Trek
- Buran Ghati Pass Trek
- Deo Tibba Peak Expedition
- Friendship Peak Expedition
- Hampta Pass Trek
- Kanamo Peak Trek Expedition
- Kareri Lake Trek
- Pin Bhaba Pass Trek
- Pin Parvati Pass Trek
- Rupin Pass Trek
- Sar Pass Trek
- Yunam Peak Trek Expedition

Triund Trek is one of the easiest trek routes in Himachal Pradesh that offers mesmerizing scenic beauty. This trek starts from Mcleodganj or Dharamkot and ends at Bhagsu Nag. Triund Hill, also known as the Crown, because it's located between Kangra Valley and Dhauladhar Mountain, is an excellent trail for trekking. A dramatic weather paired with scenic views makes the journey a memorable one. Kheer Ganga in Kasol is a beautiful, frothy-white mountain river. It falls from high up in the mountains, and the only way to reach it is via a short but arduous trek. The Kheer Ganga Trek is famed all over the country, with trekking enthusiasts raving about the beauty of it. The trek roughly is of no more than 12 km, and can be covered in no more than 5 or 6 hours if you take only a couple of short breaks.

Theory Course

Course Code: PED306TH

Kinesiology and Biomechanics

UNIT-I

Introduction of Kinesiology and Biomechanics

Meaning of Kinesiology

Kinesiologists usually use movement screens (Such as the Functional Movement Screen or Select Functional Movement Assessment), range of motion exams, specific manual muscle testing and neurological pattern testing to identify and confirm that these limitations are present and cause unwanted actions to the body when moving. Kinesiology is important to us for many reasons. It is important because it gives us to understand the movement of our body parts which helps us study how we can improve the performance and strength of athletes and people participating in sports without causing any severe damage. The increased scientific knowledge base and use of evidence-based research translates to a higher quality of care, a more comprehensive approach to your exercise, and more capability of helping you troubleshoot issues that may arise. The basic premise of kinesiology is that the body has its own healing energy and is doing its best to care for itself, but sometimes needs a little help to achieve this state. Kinesiology, therefore, may be understood as a system of natural health care which combines muscle monitoring with the principles of Chinese medicine to assess energy and body function.

Kinesiology is an interdisciplinary field that draws on concepts from fields like biology, anatomy, psychology, and nutrition to provide a comprehensive understanding of how our bodies move and how physical activity affects our overall health. Kinesiology aims to restore balance to the whole person through promoting the self-healing process. The name Kinesiology was first coined by a Swedish medical gymnast in 1854, and it's Greek for "the study of movement." A century-old sidekick to physical therapy, kinesiology has advanced through the ages to become a full-fledged academic field and a sought-after specialization within the broader health and sports sectors. Kinesiology was discovered by Dr. George Goodheart in the 1960's. He was the first to identify that there were muscles that were not 'locking' or working which meant other muscles became painful and overused. Where traditional therapies focus on the painful muscle, Kinesiology identifies the root cause of the problem – the muscles that are not functioning and uses techniques to turn those muscles on. Kinesiologists help with management of chronic conditions such as arthritis, cardiovascular disease, and diabetes through healthy lifestyle change and exercise prescription. Kinesiology means 'the study of movement'. The term is also used by complementary medicine practitioners to describe a form of therapy that uses muscle monitoring (biofeedback) to look at what may be causing 'imbalances' in the body and attempts to relieve these imbalances.

Importance of Kinesiology

- The primary focus of the kinesiology faculty is the education of students toward lifelong development of physically, mentally, emotionally, and socially fit human beings through physical activities.

- Kinesiology informs you of the relationship between the different types of levers in our skeletal system as they work with our muscles, how muscles work synergistically together and how the work with antagonists to achieve all the forms of movement and work the body can do.
- Also, an appreciation of kinesiology can help us understand injuries we sustain when we exceed the bodies limits. We study kinesiology to improve performance by learning how to analyze the movements of the human body and to discover their underlying principles.

- The study of kinesiology is an essential part of the educational experience of students of physical education, dance, sport, and physical medicine. It helps to maintain the mental and emotional balance of a person.

- Kinesiology therapy helps to boost the self-confidence of a person. Homeotherapy is used in the treatment of many recurring diseases like skin and joint diseases.

- Kinesiology also aids in treating stuttering, bed-wetting, and clumsiness in children.

- Kinesiology is, hence, very important in our lives. All the human and non-human body movements can be checked and treated using this science. The different types of treatments included in the Kinesiology treatment, help to get rid of all the common problems faced by us in our day-to-day lives. In short, it helps to energize our body and mind equally.

- It helps to get rid of the back and neck pains, which is nowadays very common in all the professions. It helps to identify the food sensitivities of our body. The various learning disabilities of a child can be easily cured by using the method of Kinesiology.

- Over-stress and anxiety are the root cause of many diseases. This can be cured with the help of Kinesiology. With a degree in Kinesiology for Individuals with Disabilities, you can use the power of adapted physical education to make a difference in the lives of the students who need it most.

Meaning of Biomechanics

Biomechanics is certainly popular right now in sports and athletics. Sports teams and athletes themselves often hire entire teams to study the movements and forces inherent in the various regular motions and important actions during the playing of a sport. Sports biomechanics studies human motion during exercise and sports. Physics and the laws of mechanics are applied to athletic performance. For example, the biomechanics of the squat includes consideration of the position and/or movement of the feet, hips, knees, back, shoulders, and arms. Knowing the correct movement patterns for a squat will help make the most of the exercise while preventing potential injuries, correcting form mistakes, and boosting results. In simplified terms, biomechanics is the science of human movement. In a sporting context, biomechanics examines an athlete in relation to his or her environment and equipment. Forces acting on the body (kinetics) and movements of the body (kinematics) are analysed prior to mapping out an exercise, performance or recovery plan. Biomechanics are equally important in the non-athletic population. Much of the way a person's joints move and function is specific to that individual and is dictated by the shape of bones and the joint surfaces, tightness or laxity of surrounding soft tissue and the function of the muscles that control the joint. Biomechanics is the science of the human living Body, including how muscles, bones, tendons, and ligaments work together to move.

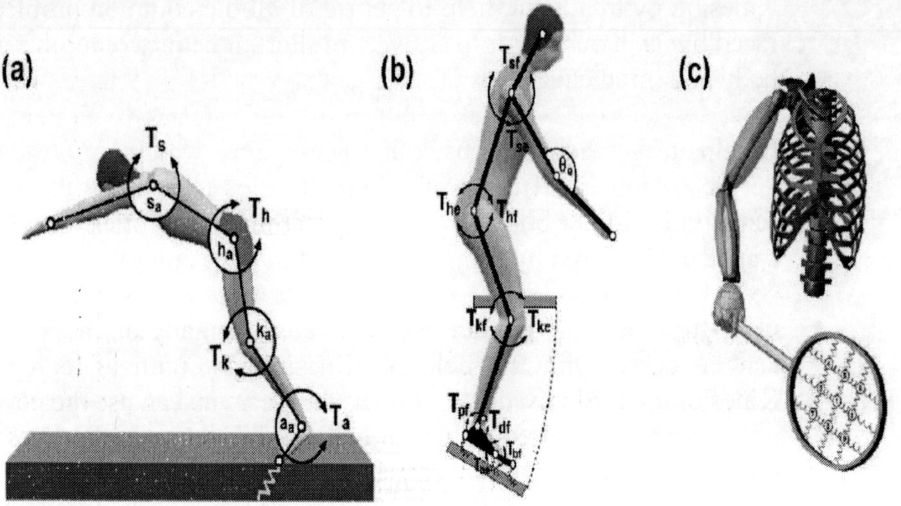

The main aim of biomechanics is to study the way the body produces force and generates movement. The discipline relies primarily on anatomy, mathematics and physics; related disciplines are anthropometry (the study of human body measurements), work physiology and kinesiology (the study of the principles of mechanics and anatomy in relation to human movement). Sports biomechanics is a subfield within biomechanics and is its own branch of human and biological science. Essentially sport and exercise biomechanics is focused on analysing the physiological mechanics of human movement. This includes analysis of how forces interact and the effects these forces have on and within the body. Professionals in sports biomechanics are generally concerned with one of two subcategories: injury prevention and performance. This group of scientists analyses the particular movements of a given sport for clues about what makes certain athletes superior to others. Biomechanics is part of the larger field of kinesiology, specifically focusing on movement mechanics. In short, it's the study and analysis of how all the individual parts of your body work together to make up athletic and everyday movements. Biomechanical testing can take place in the lab or in the field, during training or competition. Biomechanics is an interdisciplinary field that applies the principles of physics to biological systems to understand how organism move and interact with their surroundings. Biomechanics is concerned with everything from microscopic systems like muscle contraction in cells, all the way to large-scale, whole-body motions like a sprinting athlete. There are a wide variety of testing procedures in biomechanics depending upon the sport and also depending upon the skill within the sport. Testing methodology is determined based on the problem that needs to be answered and in consultation with the coach and athlete.

Importance of Biomechanics

- Biomechanics is the tool that understands human movement and has also become hugely popular amongst sports athletes as it is used to enhance athletic performance and prevent injury, too.
- Biomechanics is essentially the study of forces and their effects on the intact organism. When used in the study of sports performance, which is a quantitative-based study and analysis of athletes and different kinds of sports activities, the biomechanics used could be described as the physics of sports.
- Biomechanics in sport incorporates a detailed analysis of sport movements in order to minimise the risk of injury and improve sports performance.
- Sport and exercise biomechanics encompasses the area of science concerned with the analysis of the mechanics of human movement.
- Teacher can analyse the player's movement or action with the help of the biomechanical principles. It helps in improving the training techniques.
- It gives the knowledge of different systems of our body. For example, nervous system, muscular system and skeletal system. Biomechanics uses techniques including mathematical modelling, computer simulations, and measurements to enhance sport performance and reduce injury.
- Identify optimal movement patterns to improve sport-specific techniques.

Joints

A joint is the part of the body where two or more bones meet to allow movement. Generally speaking, the greater the range of movement, the higher the risk of injury because the strength of the joint is reduced. The six types of freely movable joint include ball and socket, saddle, hinge, pivot and gliding. The joints help us to rotate our shoulder, bend our knees and elbows, swivel our neck and more.

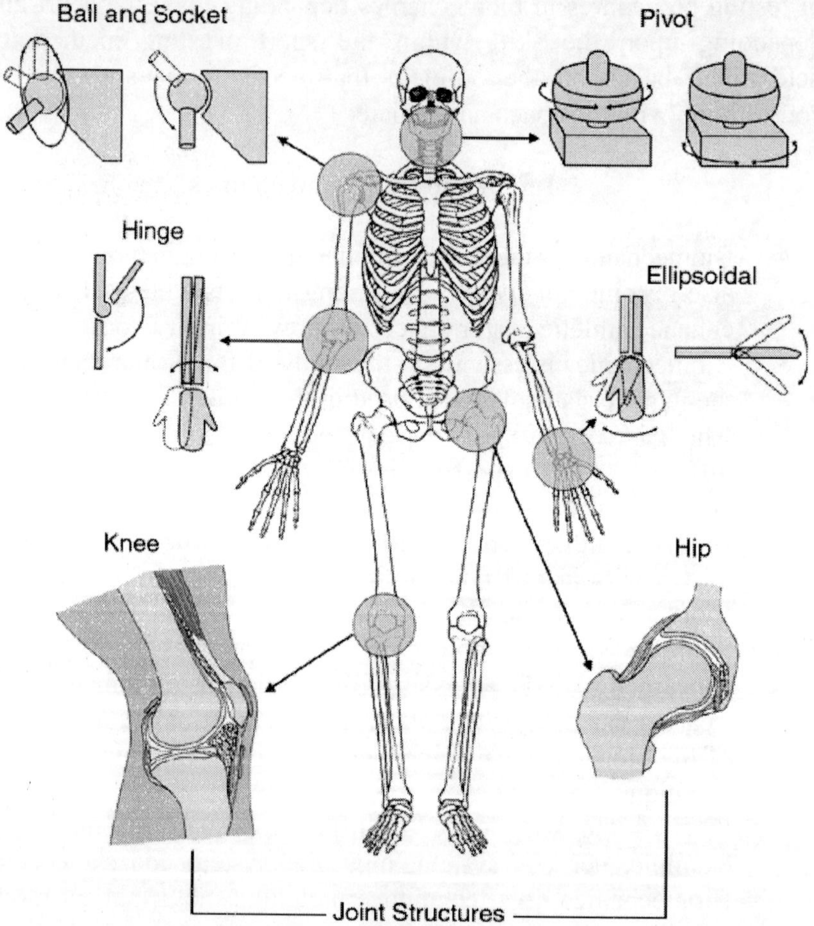

A joint is a point where two bones meet to provide a framework that permits movement. Bones are attached to one another by tissues called ligaments. Muscles are attached to bones through tendons.

Types of Joints

Ball and Socket Joints

The ball and socket joint is the type of joint with the most mobility. The smooth joint, with a hemispherical head that fits within a cuplike depression, is called the ball and socket joint. They are sometimes called spheroidal joints.

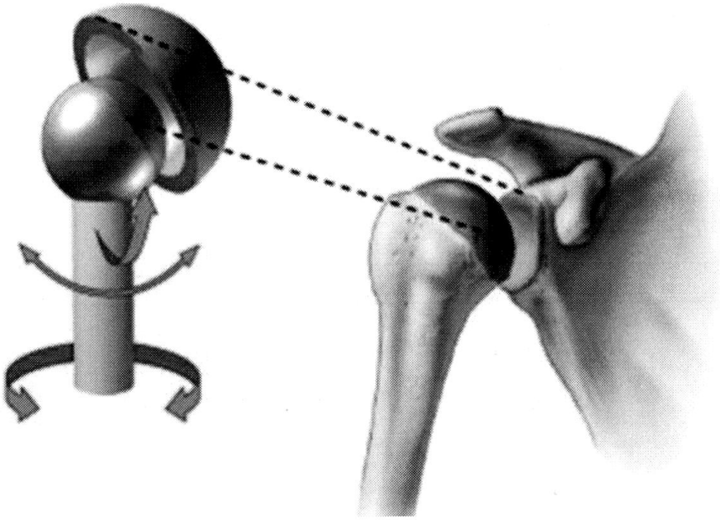

It is a joint with a rounded bone, referred to as a ball, moving within a depression of another bone, called the socket. This type of joint helps in rotational or circular movements, as one bone is captivated into the hollow space of another bone. This is the most freely moving joint. Examples of a ball and socket joint are the shoulder and the hip joint.

Pivot Joints

Pivot joints allow rotation around a single axis only and therefore mechanically speaking they possess only one degree of freedom. Pivot joint function is to allow a body part to rotate around a single point, very similar to the rotation of a wheel. Because a pivot joint rotates around a single axis, it is often known as a "rotary joint". These two bones are also joined to each other near the wrist by another pivot joint. Pivot joints hold the two bones of the forearm together. That is, a pivot joint, located near the elbow, joins the bones of the forearm (called the ulna and the radius) to each other. Pivot joints, also known as rotary joints, are a type of synovial joint that permit axial rotation. The moving bone rotates within a ring formed by the concave surface of a second bone and an adjoining ligament.

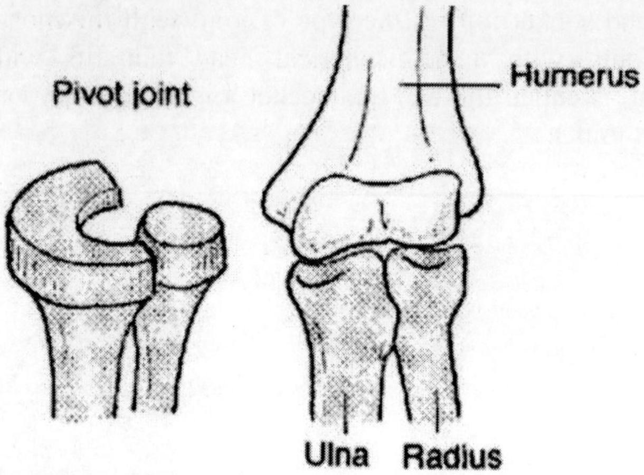

A different pivot joint, located at the base of the skull, joins the first vertebra of the spine to the second vertebra and thus permits the head to rotate (since the first vertebra is joined to the skull).

Hinge Joints

Hinge joints are classified into the category of synovial joints. A synovial joint is a kind of joint which is found between two bones that move against each other, like joints of limbs.

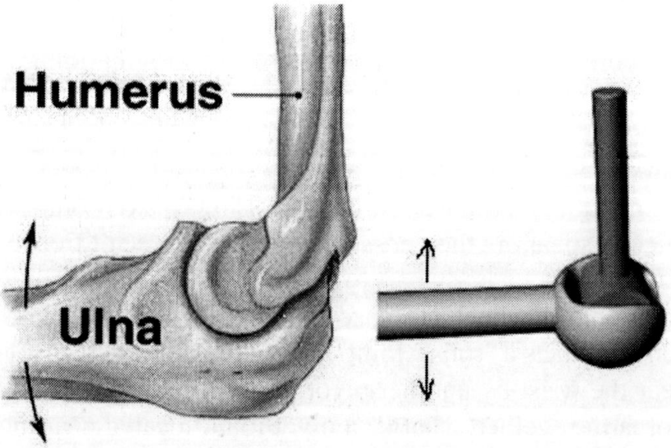

For example, shoulder, hip, elbow and knee. Therefore, a hinge joint is defined as the joint between two bones that allows movement only in one plane. For instance, human fingers, toes, elbows, knees, and ankles contain hinge joints. In such hinge joints, the bones are able to flex to decrease the angle between them like when making a fist or curling the toes and extend to increase this angle by 180 degrees while holding the foot or hand. In our body, the simplest hinge joints are the interphalangeal joints between the phalanges of the fingers and toes. A hinge joint is a type of synovial joint that exists in the body and serves to allow motion primarily in one plane. The hinge joint is made up of two or more bones with articular surfaces that are covered by hyaline cartilage and lubricated by synovial fluid. Hinge joints are a type of joint that functions much like the hinge on a door, allowing bones to move in one direction back and forth with limited motion along other planes. The fingers, toes, elbows, knees, and ankles contain hinge joints.

Saddle Joints

Saddle joints provide stability to the bones while providing more flexibility than a hinge or gliding joint. The bone sitting on the saddle can move in an oval shape relative to the other bone, similar to a Condyloid joint.

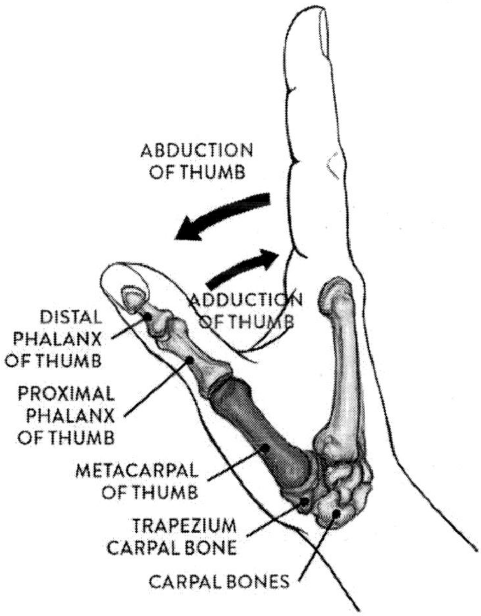

A saddle joint is a type of biaxial and movable joint that allows movements on two planes–flexion or extension and abduction or adduction. This joint is mainly formed between the bones, whose articulating surfaces have both concave and convex regions. Saddle joints are another type of synovial joint. The saddle joint gets its name because the bone forming one part of the joint is concave (turned inward) at one end and looks like a saddle. The other bone's end is convex (turned outward), and looks like a rider in a saddle.

Ellipsoid Joints

Ellipsoid joint is a biaxial joint that enables movements in angular motions. Movement of these joints are in two plains: back and front, and side to side.

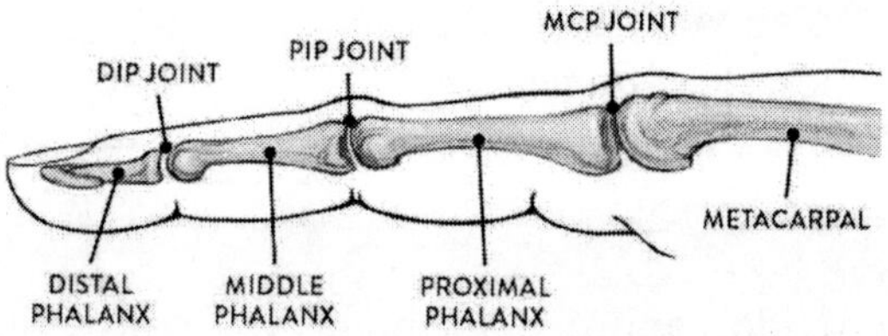

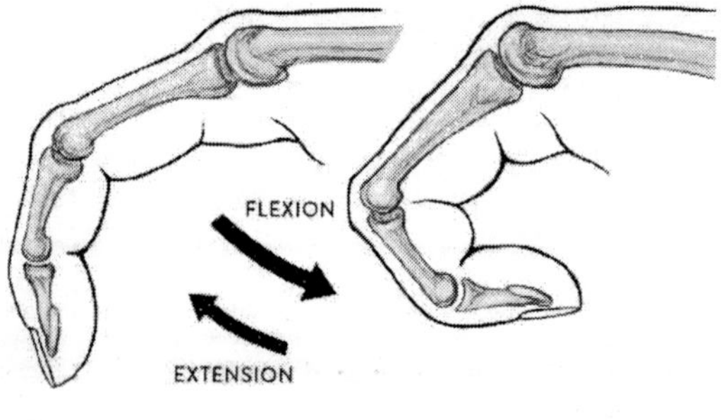

An ellipsoid joint is located between knuckle joints, wrist joints, and metacarpophalangeal and metatarsophalangeal joints in fingers. It is a type of synovial joint and a most important type of joint. It is also called the curved joint. As per the name, ellipsoid joints move in an elliptical order. This is also referred to as Condyloid or Condylar joints.

Gliding Joints

Gliding joints move with a gliding motion. They are also known as either arthrodial joints or plane joints, and usually occur between flat bones that need to slide past each other in order to allow the desired motion. The movement i.e. gliding joint movement that occurs between gliding joints is limited by the ligaments that hold the bones together. The primary places in the human body that you will find gliding joints are in the ankles, wrist, and spine.

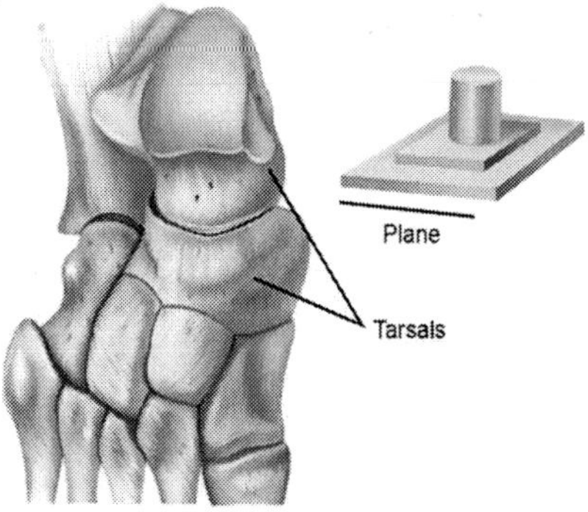

A gliding joint is a synovial joint in which the bony surfaces that the joint holds together are flat, or only slightly rounded. (A synovial joint is the living material that holds two or more bones together but also permits these bones to move relative to each other.).

Movements around Joints

Flexion & Extension

Flexion describes a bending movement that decreases the angle between a segment and its proximal segment. Extension is the opposite of flexion, describing a straightening movement that increases the angle between body parts. Flexion and extension describe movements that affect the angle between two parts of the body.

Abduction & Adduction

Abduction refers to a motion that pulls a structure or part away from the midline of the body. In the case of fingers and toes, it refers to spreading the digits apart, away from the centreline of the hand or foot. Adduction refers to a motion that pulls a structure or part toward the midline of the body, or towards the midline of a limb. Abduction is the motion of a structure away from the midline while adduction refers to motion towards the center of the body. The center of the body is defined as the midsagittal plane. These terms come from Latin words with similar meanings, ab- being the Latin prefix indicating "away," ad- indicating "toward," and ducere meaning "to draw or pull" (cf. English words "duct," "conduct," "induction").

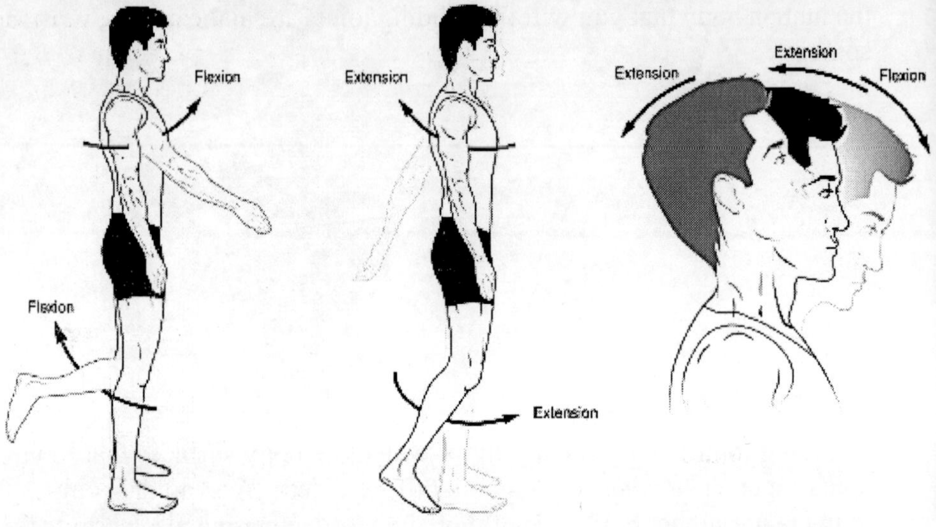

(a) and (b) Angular movements: flexion and extension at the shoulder and knees

(c) Angular movements: flexion and extension of the neck

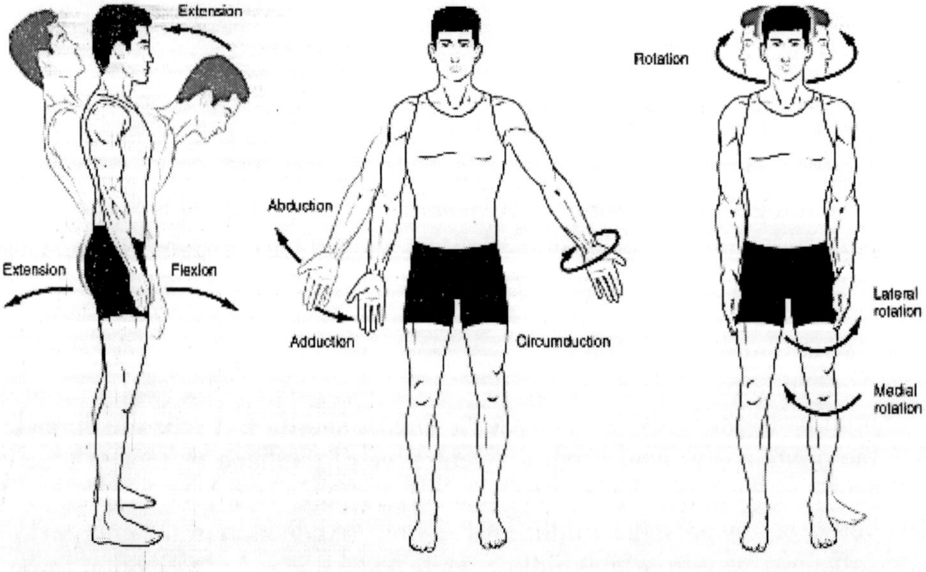

(d) Angular movements: flexion and extension of the vertebral column

(e) Angular movements: abduction, adduction, and circumduction of the upper limb at the shoulder

(f) Rotation of the head, neck, and lower limb

Circumduction

Circumduction is the movement of a body region in a circular manner, in which one end of the body region being moved stays relatively stationary while the other end describes a circle. It involves the sequential combination of flexion, adduction, extension, and abduction at a joint. This type of motion is found at biaxial condyloid and saddle joints, and at multiaxial ball-and-sockets joints.

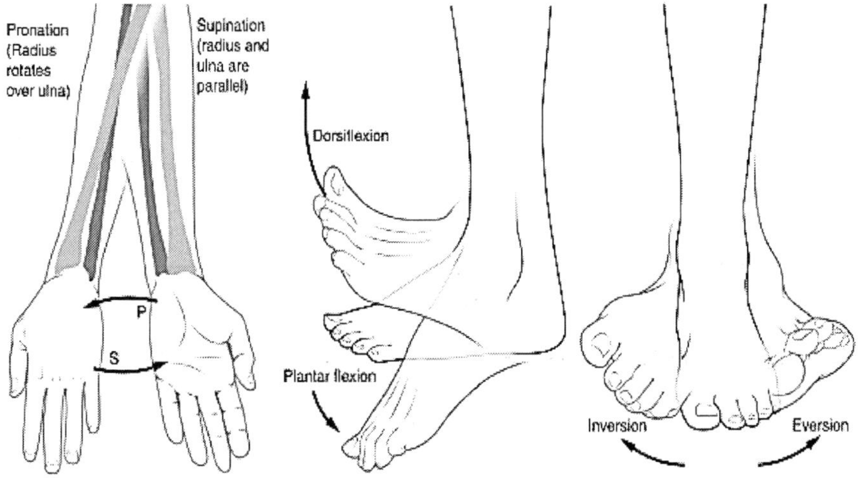

(g) Pronation (P) and supination (S) (h) Dorsiflexion and plantar flexion (i) Inversion and eversion

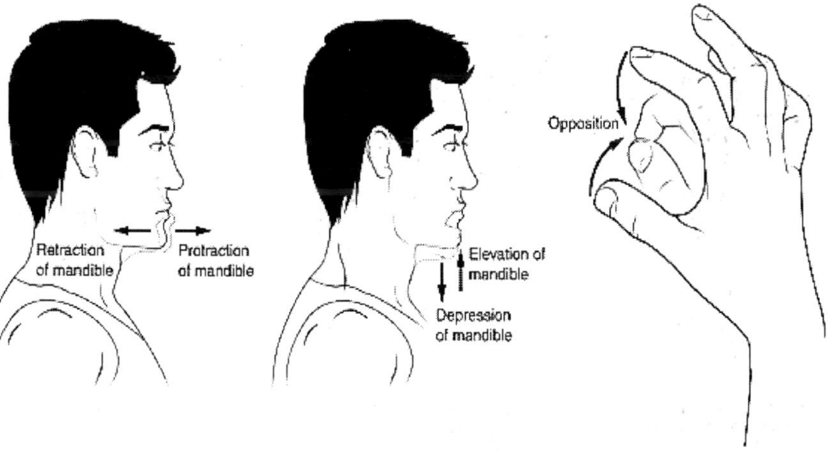

(j) Protraction and retraction (k) Elevation and depression (l) Opposition

Rotation

Rotation can occur within the vertebral column, at a pivot joint, or at a ball-and-socket joint. Rotation of the neck or body is the twisting movement produced by the summation of the small rotational movements available between adjacent vertebrae. At a pivot joint, one bone rotates in relation to another bone. This is a uniaxial joint, and thus rotation is the only motion allowed at a pivot joint.

Supination and Pronation

Supination and pronation are movements of the forearm. In the anatomical position, the upper limb is held next to the body with the palm facing forward. This is the supinated position of the forearm. In this position, the radius and ulna are parallel to each other. When the palm of the hand faces backward, the forearm is in the pronated position, and the radius and ulna form an X-shape.

Dorsiflexion and Plantar Flexion

Dorsiflexion and plantar flexion are movements at the ankle joint, which is a hinge joint. Lifting the front of the foot, so that the top of the foot moves toward the anterior leg is dorsiflexion, while lifting the heel of the foot from the ground or pointing the toes downward is plantar flexion. These are the only movements available at the ankle joint.

Protraction and Retraction

Retraction is the opposite motion, with the scapula being pulled posteriorly and medially, toward the vertebral column. For the mandible, protraction occurs when the lower jaw is pushed forward, to stick out the chin, while retraction pulls the lower jaw backward. Protraction and retraction are anterior-posterior movements of the scapula or mandible. Protraction of the scapula occurs when the shoulder is moved forward, as when pushing against something or throwing a ball.

Inversion and Eversion

Inversion is the turning of the foot to angle the bottom of the foot toward the midline, while eversion turns the bottom of the foot away from the midline. The foot has a greater range of inversion than eversion motion.

Inversion and eversion are complex movements that involve the multiple plane joints among the tarsal bones of the posterior foot (intertarsal joints) and thus are not motions that take place at the ankle joint.

Opposition and Reposition

Opposition is the thumb movement that brings the tip of the thumb in contact with the tip of a finger. This movement is produced at the first carpometacarpal joint, which is a saddle joint formed between the trapezium carpal bone and the first metacarpal bone. Thumb opposition is produced by a combination of flexion and abduction of the thumb at this joint. Returning the thumb to its anatomical position next to the index finger is called reposition.

Goniometry

Goniometry is the art and science of measuring the joint ranges in each plane of the joint. The term 'goniometry' is derived from the greek words 'gonia' meaning angle and 'metron' meaning measure, therefore goniometry refers to the measurement of angles, which in rehabilitation settings refers to the measurement of angles in each plane at the joints of the body. A goniometer is a device used in physical therapy to measure a joint's range of motion (ROM). There are two "arms" one that is stationary and one that is movable that are hinged together. Each is positioned at specific points on the body with the center of the goniometer aligned at the joint of interest. The therapists most frequently use a goniometer for the measurement of the range of motion. If the patient has an altered range of motion in a particular joint, the therapist uses a goniometer to assess the range of motion during the initial assessment and then uses the goniometer in subsequent sessions to ensure the procedure is working and to assess the effectiveness of the procedure.

UNIT-II
Axis and Planes

Fundamental anatomical position

Anatomical position is the description of any region or part of the body in a specific stance. In the anatomical position, the body is upright, directly facing the observer, feet flat and directed forward. The upper limbs are at the body's sides with the palms facing forward.

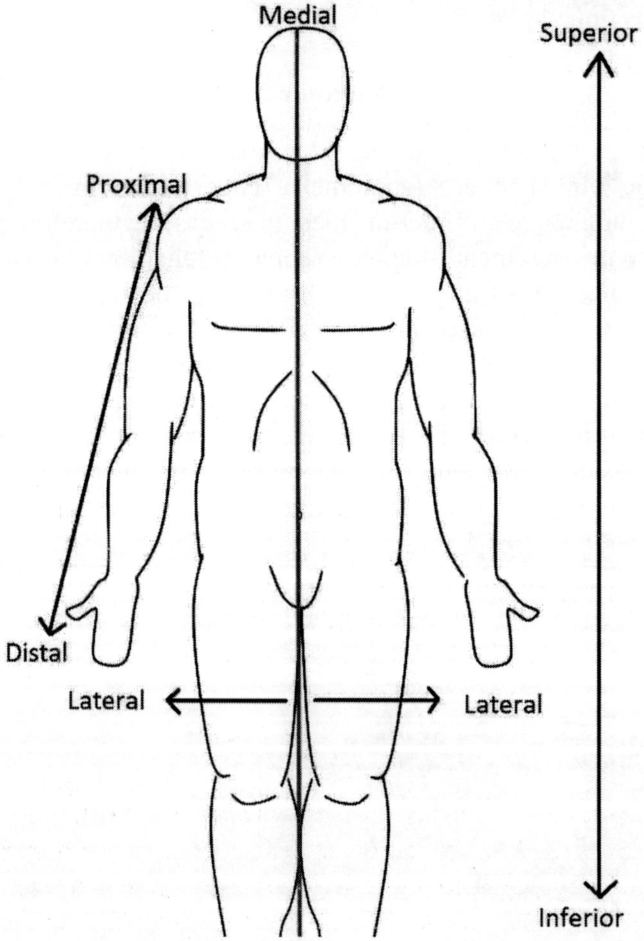

The anatomical position, also known as standard anatomical position, is the consistent position of the human body in which positional reference is made for anatomical nomenclature. It is not reliant on whether the patient is standing, supine, prone, sitting, etc. Standard anatomical position is the body orientation used when describing an organism's anatomy. Standardization is necessary to avoid confusion since most organisms can take on many different positions that may change the relative placement of organs. All descriptions refer to the organism in its standard anatomical position, even when the organism's appendages are in another position.

Planes

The anatomical position is used as a reference when describing locations of structures and movements. It is an upright position with arms by the side and palms facing forward. Feet are parallel with toes facing forward.

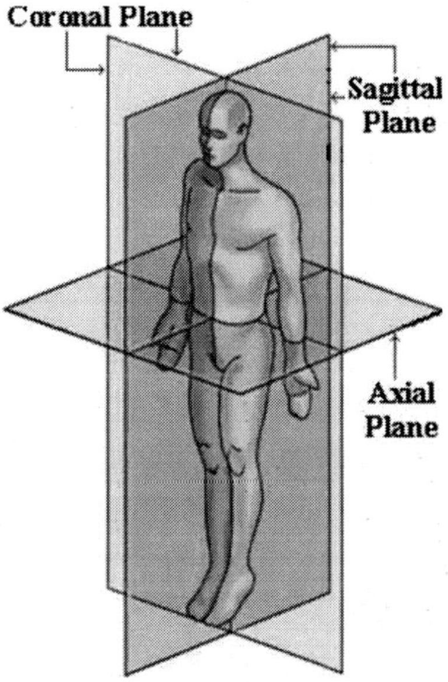

The human body is described by three planes (sagittal or anterior posterior, horizontal or transverse, frontal or lateral). Planes of the human body can be cut up, physically and metaphorically, for research and diagnostic purposes. Anatomical planes are imaginary planes/2D surfaces used to divide the body to facilitate descriptions of location and movement. Three basic reference planes are used in anatomy. A sagittal plane, also known as the longitudinal plane, is perpendicular to the ground and divides the body into left and right. The midsagittal or median plane is in the midline i.e. it would pass through the midline structures (e.g. navel or spine), and all other sagittal planes (also referred to as parasagittal planes) are parallel to it. Median can also refer to the midsagittal plane of other structures, such as a digit. The sagittal plane in the midline provides the basis of assessment of most of the parameters required in assessing the positions of the pelvic viscera. A coronal or frontal plane is perpendicular to the ground and divides the body into dorsal (posterior or back) and ventral (anterior or front) portions. A vertical line which divides the body into a front (anterior) section and back (posterior) section. A transverse plane, also known as an axial plane or cross-section, divides the body into cranial (head) and caudal (tail) portions. It is parallel to the ground, which (in humans) separates the superior from the inferior, or put another way, the head from the feet.

Axis

An axis is a straight line around which an object rotates. Movement at the joint takes place in a plane about an axis. There are three axes of rotation.

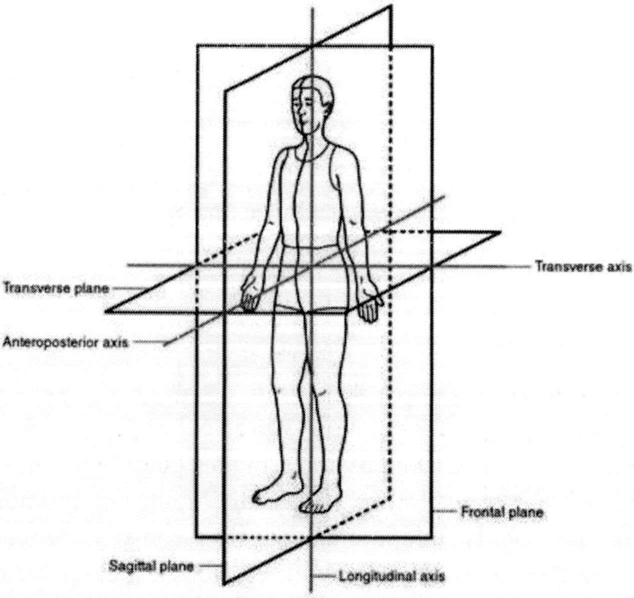

Sagittal axis

Passes horizontally from posterior to anterior and is formed by the intersection of the sagittal and transverse planes.

Frontal axis

Passes horizontally from left to right and is formed by the intersection of the frontal and transverse planes.

Vertical axis

Passes vertically from inferior to superior and is formed by the intersection of the sagittal and frontal planes.

Kinesiological Classification of Muscles

The muscular system is a system that includes muscle cells and muscle tissues. The human body's muscular system consists of specific cells called muscle fibers.

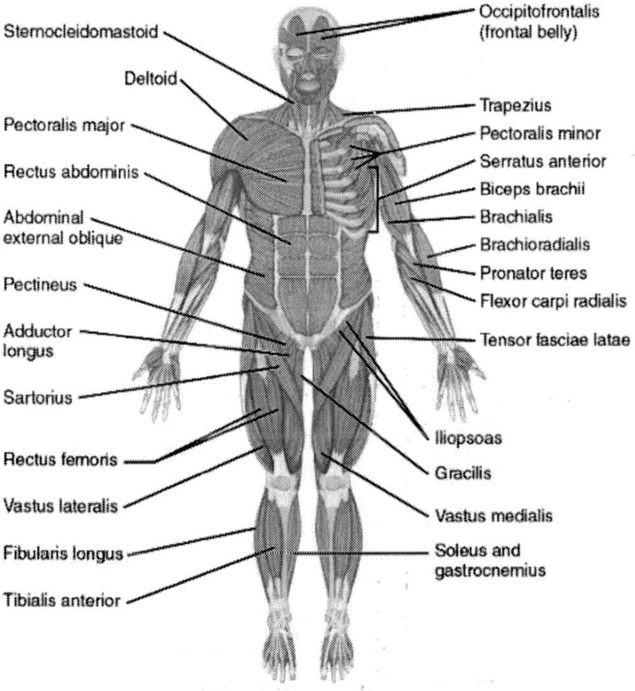

The muscular system is composed of specialized cells called muscle fibers. Their predominant function is contractibility. Muscles, attached to bones or internal organs and blood vessels, are responsible for movement. Nearly all movement in the body is the result of muscle contraction. Every muscle is a different organ made of blood vessels, skeletal muscle tissue, nerves, and tendons. Muscle tissues are found in the heart, blood vessels, and digestive system. The muscular system is responsible for the movement of the human body. Attached to the bones of the skeletal system are about 700 named muscles that make up roughly half of a person's body weight. Each of these muscles is a discrete organ constructed of skeletal muscle tissue, blood vessels, tendons, and nerves. The main function of the muscular system is the motor function. By the contraction of muscle fibers, it helps the body to perform daily activities. However, not only the human muscular system is responsible for the motor function in the body, but it is connected with other organ locations in the body in other systems, such as bones in the skeletal system.

Skeletal Muscles

The skeletal muscles protect the internal organs and tissues from any injury and also provide support to these delicate organs and tissues. Each skeletal muscle consists of thousands of muscle fibers wrapped together by connective tissue sheaths. The individual bundles of muscle fibers in a skeletal muscle are known as fasciculi. The outermost connective tissue sheath surrounding the entire muscle is known as epimysium. The connective tissue sheath covering each fasciculus is known as perimysium, and the innermost sheath surrounding individual muscle fiber is known as endomysium. Skeletal muscles vary considerably in size, shape, and arrangement of fibers. They range from extremely tiny strands such as the stapedium muscle of the middle ear to large masses such as the muscles of the thigh. Some skeletal muscles are broad in shape and some narrow. Skeletal muscle is a specialized contractile tissue found in animals which functions to move an organism's body. Skeletal muscle is comprised from a series of bundles of muscle fibers, surrounded by protective membranes. This arrangement allows skeletal muscle to contract quickly and release quickly without subjecting the individual fibers to too much friction. Skeletal muscle tissue can be found across the animal kingdom, in most multi-cellular forms of life. Skeletal muscles are attached to bones by tendons, and they produce all the movements of body parts in relation to each other. Unlike smooth muscle and cardiac muscle, skeletal muscle is under voluntary control.

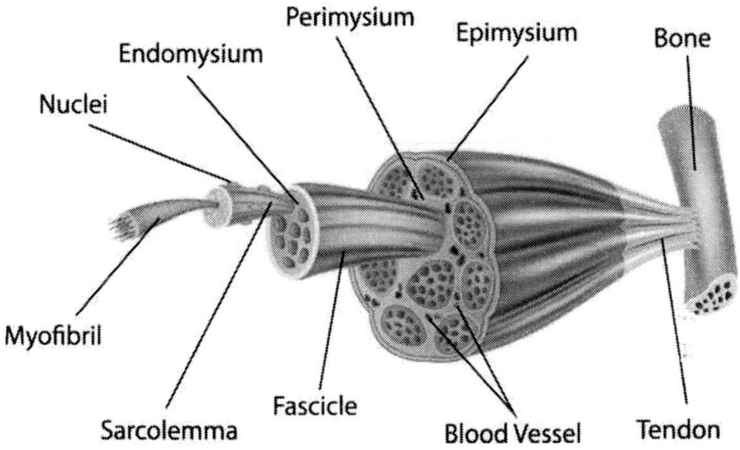

Skeletal muscles comprise 30 to 40% of your total body mass. They're the muscles that connect to your bones and allow you to perform a wide range of movements and functions. Skeletal muscles are voluntary, meaning you control how and when they work.

They serve a variety of functions, including:

- Chewing and swallowing, which are the first parts of digestion.
- Expanding and contracting your chest cavity so you can inhale and exhale at will.
- Maintaining body posture.
- Moving the bones in different parts of your body.
- Protecting joints and holding them in place.

Generally speaking, skeletal muscles come in four main shapes, including:

Triangular – wider at the bottom, tapered at the top, such as the deltoid muscles of the shoulder.
Circular – a ring-shape like a doughnut, such as the muscles that surround the mouth, the pupils and the anus. These are also known as sphincters.
Spindle – wide through the middle and tapering at both ends, such as the biceps on the front of the upper arm.

Flat – like a sheet, such as the diaphragm that separates the chest from the abdominal cavity.

The primary functions of the skeletal muscle take place via its intrinsic excitation-contraction coupling process. As the muscle is attached to the bone tendons, the contraction of the muscle leads to movement of that bone that allows for the performance of specific movements. The skeletal muscle also provides structural support and helps in maintaining the posture of the body. Skeletal muscle is found between bones, and uses tendons to connect the epimysium to the periosteum, or outer covering, of bone.Skeletal muscle includes the tissue fibers attached to your skeleton or bones and is responsible for all your movements. These muscles are also found at the openings of tracts in your body, like your throat, anus, and urethra. They're often called voluntary muscles because you control when and how they work. Skeletal muscle, as the name implies, is any muscles that connects to and controls the motions of the skeleton. In all there are somewhere between 600 and 900 muscles in the human body, but an exact number is hard. Many muscles are obscurely small or are sometimes grouped together with similar muscles.

Cardiac Muscles

The cardiac muscle is made up of cells that are specialized for contraction and pumping. They contract in intervals to pump blood through the heart and into the rest of the body. Cardiac muscles also contain a specialized cell which help transmit electrical impulses to and from the heart muscle cells, making them an important component in the functioning of the heart. Cardiac muscle makes up the thick middle layer of the heart. It is one of three types of muscle in the body, along with skeletal and smooth muscle. The myocardium is surrounded by a thin outer layer called the epicardium and an inner endocardium. Cardiac muscle is able to contract and relax, unlike skeletal muscles which only contract. This means that cardiac tissue will have far more irregular shapes than skeletal muscles. Cardiac muscle tissue is only found in your heart, where it performs coordinated contractions that allow your heart to pump blood through your circulatory system. Cardiac muscle tissue works to keep your heart pumping through involuntary movements. This is one feature that differentiates it from skeletal muscle tissue, which you can control. Cardiac muscle tissue gets its strength and flexibility from its interconnected cardiac muscle cells, or fibers. Cardiac muscle is made up of specialised cells called cardio myocytes. These cells are sometimes called contractile myofibrils because they are long and cylindrical (shaped like a fibril) and they contract at a regular rate to keep blood flowing through the heart.

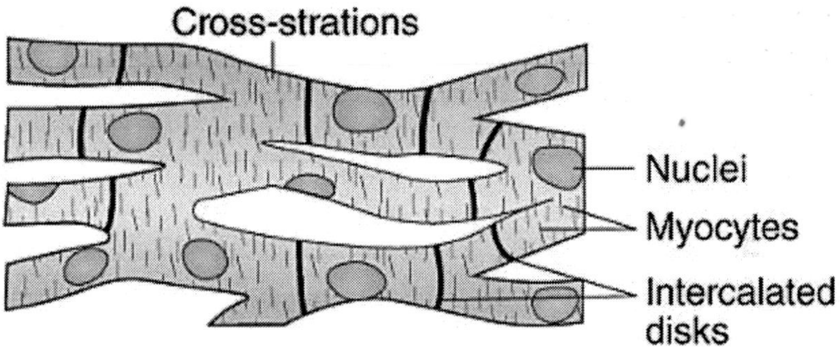

The contractile functional unit of myofibril is known as the sarcomere. Cardiac muscle is very different from skeletal muscle because it has a much more complex structure.

Smooth muscles

Smooth muscles contract to regulate blood pressure and other cardiovascular processes. They also aid in food digestion through peristalsis, which is the rhythmic wave-like contraction of muscles around the digestive tract. The smooth muscles return to normal length after stretching. They can come back to their original size as they have elasticity. Smooth muscles are located in the internal lining of different hollow organs like the reproductive system, the urinary bladder, liver, and the circulatory system's blood vessels, where vascular smooth muscles are oriented in a circle around the vascular lumen and form numerous layers. In the eyes, they can change iris size and lens shape. It is also present in the skin, allowing the hair to stand straight in reaction to cooler conditions or worries. Smooth muscle is a type of non-striated muscle that is found in the walls of hollow organs and blood vessels. Smooth muscle can be found throughout the body but is most common around the digestive tract, in the walls of blood vessels, arteries, and around other organs such as the eyes. Smooth muscle is present throughout the body, where it serves a variety of functions. It is in the stomach and intestines, where it helps with digestion and nutrient collection. It exists throughout the urinary system, where it functions to help rid the body of toxins and works in electrolyte balance. Smooth muscle tissue, unlike skeletal or cardiac tissues, does not have clearly defined striations visible on the cells. This is because smooth muscle cells are organized in a different way than other muscle cells. The actin and myosin filaments in smooth muscle are arranged in a stacked pattern across the cell.

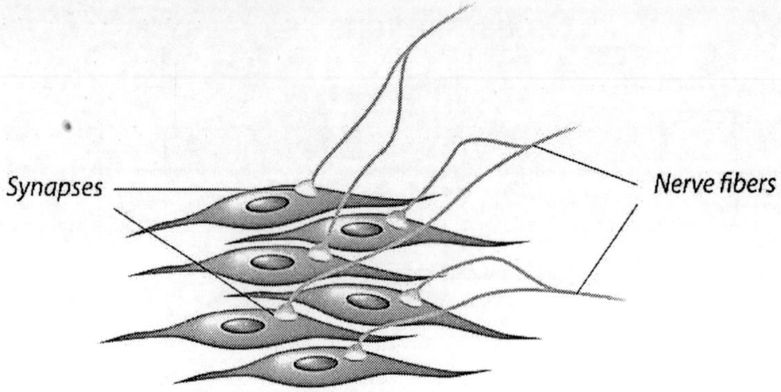

Multiunit Smooth Muscle

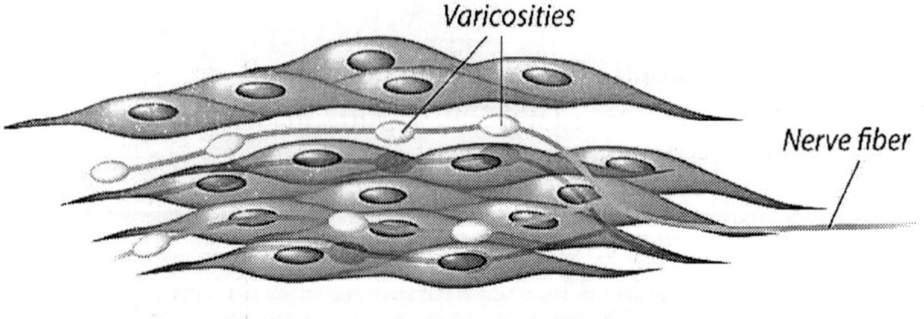

Single-unit Smooth Muscle

Smooth muscle is found throughout the body where it serves a variety of functions:

- It is found throughout arteries and veins where it plays a vital role in the regulation of blood pressure and tissue oxygenation.
- It is in the stomach and intestines where it helps with digestion and nutrient collection.
- It is found throughout the urinary system where it functions to help rid the body of toxins and works in electrolyte balance.

Smooth muscle cells lack the striated banding pattern found in cardiac and skeletal muscle, and they receive neural innervation from the autonomic nervous system. In addition, the contractile state of smooth muscle is controlled by hormones, autocrine/paracrine agents, and other local chemical signals. Smooth muscle cells also develop tonic and phasic contractions in response to changes in load or length. Smooth muscle is a type of muscle tissue which is used by various systems to apply pressure to vessels and organs. Smooth muscle is composed of sheets or strands of smooth muscle cells. These cells have fibers of actin and myosin which run through the cell and are supported by a framework of other proteins. The vasculature system that transports blood throughout the body is controlled by smooth muscle.

Role of different muscles

Agonist

In the fastest movements, the agonist muscle is primarily responsible for the distance moved, while the antagonist muscle provides an effective means of reducing movement time.

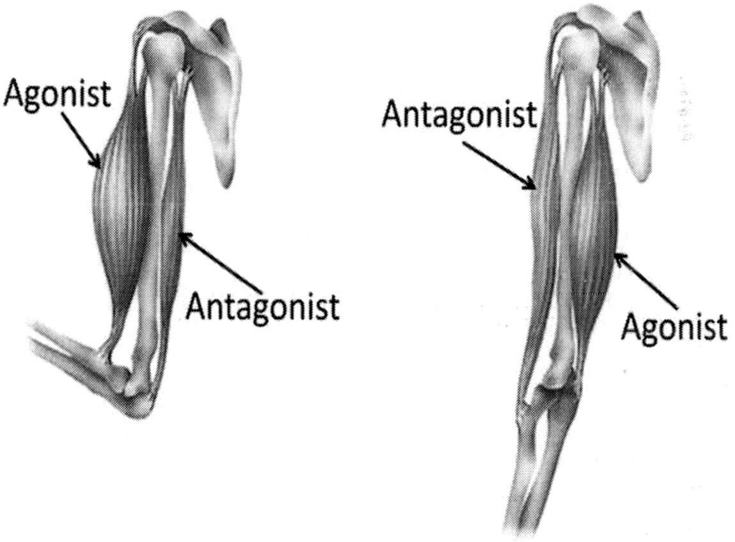

An agonist muscle is a muscle that contracts to provide the main force to move or rotate a bone through its joint. An antagonist muscle is a muscle that produces the opposite action of an agonist.

Antagonist

An antagonist is a muscle that produces the opposite action of an agonist. When an agonist muscle contracts and shortens to move a body part, an antagonist will relax and lengthen to allow the movement to occur.

Mover

The prime mover, sometimes called the agonist, is the muscle that provides the primary force driving the action. An antagonist muscle is in opposition to a prime mover in that it provides some resistance and/or reverses a given movement.

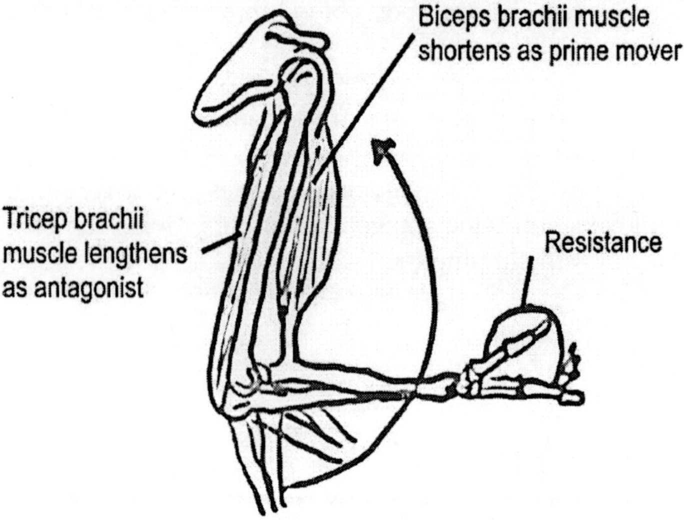

Prime movers and antagonists are often paired up on opposite sides of a joint, with their prime mover/antagonist roles reversing as the movement changes direction.

Stabilizer

In any movement, stabilizer muscles act to stabilize one joint so the desired movement can be performed in another joint. These muscles usually aren't directly involved in a movement, but work to keep you steady so that your primary muscles can do their job. When it comes to working out and fitness, most people primarily think about strengthening those muscles that move the body. Yet, it's the stabilizing muscles that hold your body upright and in control enough to even perform those squats while you're weightlifting or that tree pose during yoga.

Fixator

The muscle which fixes the attachments of the agonists, antagonists, and synergists. In the human body, we have so many examples of fixator muscles. The muscles attached to the shoulder girdle to the trunk acts as the fixator for the deltoid action. Fixators are not only fixing the bony component while the movement of agonists, antagonists or synergists and also have dynamic properties.

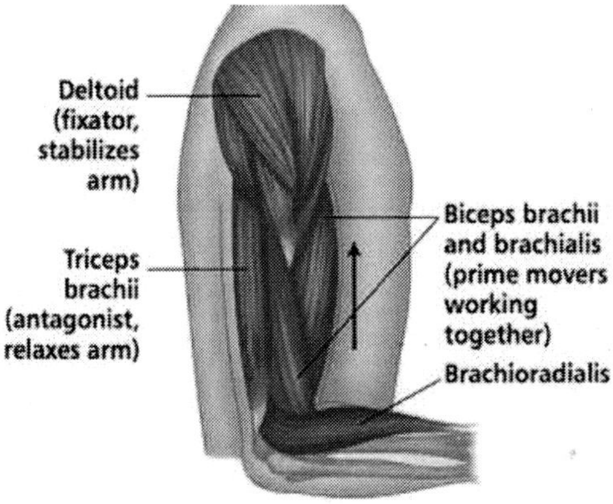

The fixator in a movement is the muscle stabilizes the origin of the agonist and the joint that the origin spans (moves over-prime movers) in order to help the agonist function most effectively with fewer efforts. For the bicep curl, this would be the rotator cuff muscles, the 'guardians of the shoulder joint.

Neutralizer

Neutralizers are muscles that oppose unwanted joint motions created by the prime mover and/or synergists, and/or muscles that prevent unwanted ancillary motion. Neutralizing muscles provide important support during exercise to prevent injury and restrict movement. These muscles are often smaller than the large moving muscles of your body; however, their importance should not be underappreciated in a training program.

UNIT-III
Biomechanical Terms

Description of biomechanical terms:

Distance and Displacement

Distance refers to "how much ground an object has covered" during its motion while Displacement refers to how far out of place an object is. Distance is a Scalar quantity whereas Displacement is a Vector quantity.

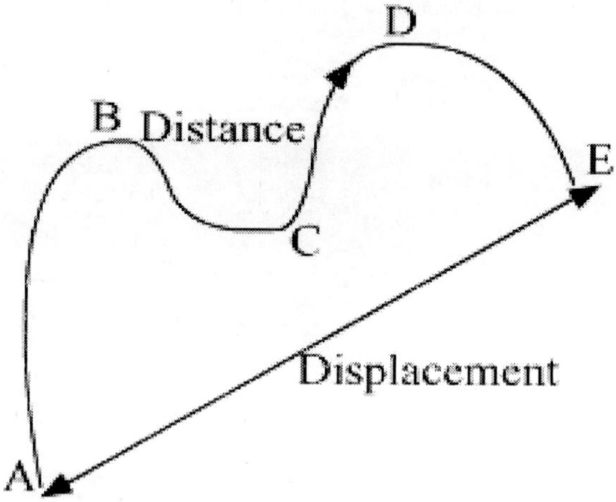

Distance measures the length of the path that an object takes without regard for the starting or ending place, or the direction of its travel. Displacement is the measure of an object's change in position from an initial starting point to an ending point with regard to the direction of its travel. Distance is the total movement of an object without any regard to direction. We can define distance as to how much ground an object has covered despite its starting or ending point. Displacement is defined as the change in position of an object. It is a vector quantity and has a direction and magnitude. It is represented as an arrow that points from the starting position to the final position. The distance travelled is the magnitude of the displacement. So it is always positive. The displacement of an object can be zero if the initial and final position is the same but the distance travelled may not be equal to zero.

Speed

Speed is a measure of the rate of change of the distance travelled by a moving object. Speed is a scalar, which means that it is a unit of measurement that has magnitude but does not have direction. The speed of a body which is gathered in a relatively shorter period of time or in an instance is known as instantaneous speed of a body.

$$\text{Speed} = \frac{\text{Distance}}{\text{Time}}$$

$$\text{Distance} = \text{Speed} \times \text{Time}$$

$$\text{Time} = \frac{\text{Distance}}{\text{Speed}}$$

Speed is a scalar quantity that refers to "how fast an object is moving." Speed can be thought of as the rate at which an object covers distance. A fast-moving object has a high speed and covers a relatively large distance in a short amount of time. Speed is measured as the ratio of distance to the time in which the distance was covered. Speed is a scalar quantity as it has only direction and no magnitude.

Velocity

Velocity is a vector measurement of the rate of motion of an object and the direction in which it is moving. Hence, to determine the velocity as per this definition, we should be familiar with both the magnitude and direction. Velocity is a vector measure of the speed and direction of movement. Simply put, velocity is the pace at which something moves in a particular direction. The speed of a car going north on a major highway and the speed of a rocket bursting into space may both be measured using speed. As one may anticipate, the scalar size (total value) of vector velocity represents the speed of movement.

$$\text{Velocity} = \frac{\text{Displacement}}{\text{Time}}$$

or

$$v = \frac{s}{t}$$

Velocity is a vector quantity that refers to "the rate at which an object changes its position." Imagine a person moving rapidly one step forward and one step back always returning to the original starting position. While this might result in a frenzy of activity, it would result in a zero velocity.

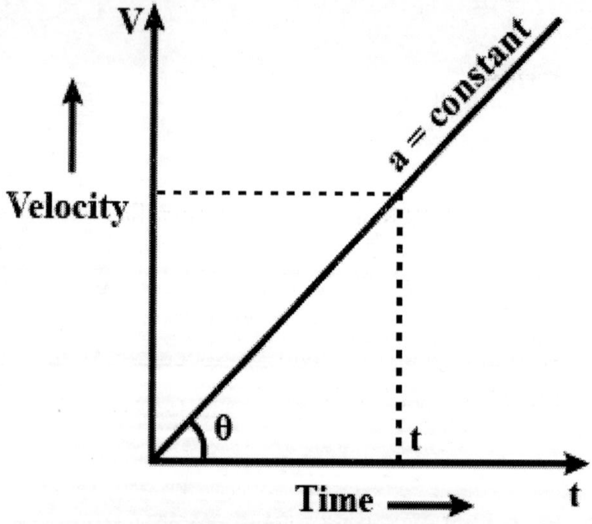

$$\tan\theta = \frac{v}{t} = a\ (\text{acceleration})$$

Speed can be calculated using a simple formula using measurement, distance, and time. Unlike speed, velocity measures displacement, a vector quantity indicating the difference between an object's final and initial positions. Speed measures distance, a scalar quantity that measures the total length of an object's path. In terms of computations, speed is the first exit of a place in terms of time.

Acceleration

Acceleration can also be termed as the rate of change in velocity and the change over time. An acceleration vector's magnitude tells us how much the velocity will change, while its direction tells us how the velocity will change i.e. whether the velocity is increasing or decreasing, the velocity vector is changing direction, or some combination of the three.

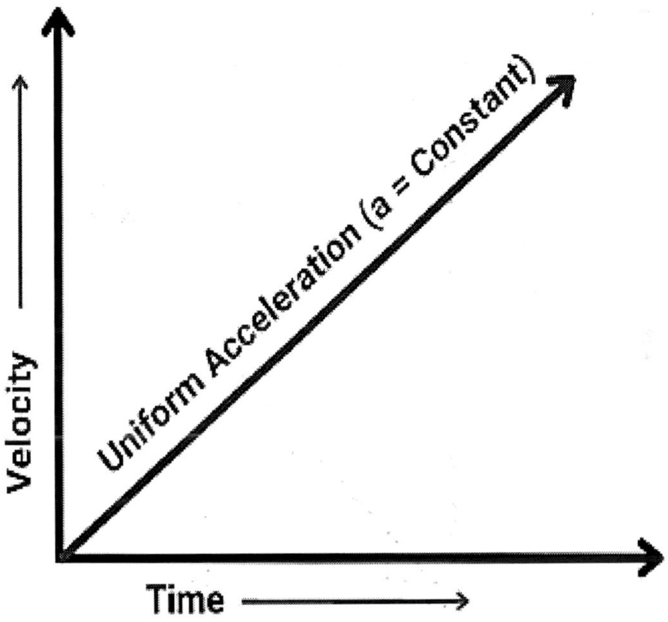

Acceleration is the change in speed or velocity of an object over a certain time. It can be calculated by dividing the change in velocity by the total time. When an object is travelling in a straight line with an increase in velocity at equal intervals of time, then the object is said to be in uniform acceleration. Free falling of an object is an example of uniform acceleration. If either of the conditions of motion by the object is contented then the object is said to be in acceleration. Acceleration is sometimes perplexed with speeding up of the object only. Acceleration pertains to a change in the momentum of an object within a given period. As a vector quantity, acceleration implicates both transitions in the speed and the direction of the object that is in motion. Acceleration is a vector quantity as it has both magnitude and direction. It is also the second derivative of position with respect to time or it is the first derivative of velocity with respect to time. The average acceleration over a period of time is defined as the total change in velocity in the given interval divided by the total time taken for the change.

Angular Velocity

Angular velocity is an important physics concept that is applied to objects that move along a circular path. The amount of change of angular displacement of the particle at a given period of time is called angular velocity. The track of the angular velocity vector is vertical to the plane of rotation, in a direction which is usually indicated by the right-hand rule.

Angular Acceleration

Angular Acceleration is defined as the time rate of change of angular velocity. It is usually expressed in radians per second per second. Angular acceleration, also called rotational acceleration, is a quantitative expression of the change in angular velocity that a spinning object undergoes per unit time. It is a vector quantity, consisting of a magnitude component and either of two defined directions or senses.

Linear and Angular Motion

Linear motion is any motion that moves along a straight line in one direction. The direction can either be horizontal vertical or inclined direction. Example approach run. Angular motion is rotatory motion it occurs when all points on a body or object move in a circular path about the same fixed central line or axis. A child swings and rotations in hammer throw are the best example.

Kinetics and Kinematics

Kinetics is focused on understanding the cause of different types of motions of an object, such as rotational motion in which the object experiences force or torque. Kinematics explains the terms such as acceleration, velocity, and position of objects. The mass of the object is not considered while studying kinematics. Kinematics uses common physics-based variables to describe motion concerning space and time. These variables can refer to a single point, a body segment, a joint, a limb, or the whole body. The main basic kinematic variables in biomechanics are position, velocity, and acceleration. Each of them can be linear or angular. They can also be either local or global. Kinematics and kinetics are sub-areas of biomechanics. Kinematics is the study of description of motion while kinetics is the study of explanation of motion. Kinetics, also called dynamics, is a vital part of mechanics that deals with the function of different forces and torques on an object in motion. As a matter of fact, an object moves only when these forces create movement. In kinematics, the focus is on the motion of the object, while kinetics focuses on the cause of motion.

Force

Force is an external agent capable of changing a body's state of rest or motion. It has a magnitude and a direction. A force is a push or pull upon an object resulting from the object's interaction with another object.

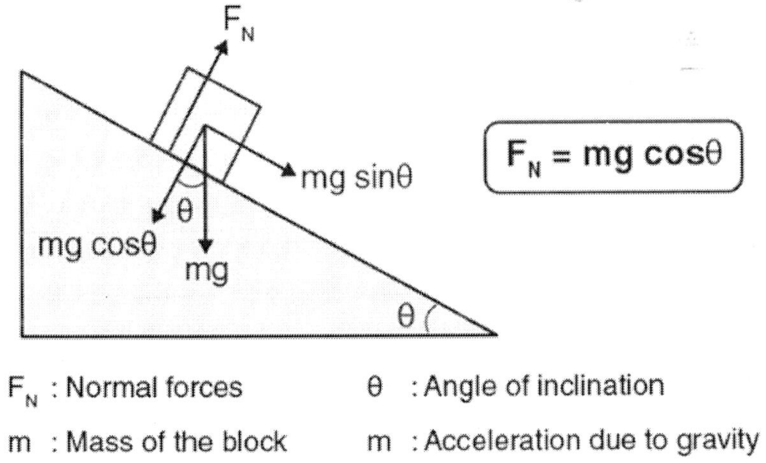

Whenever there is an interaction between two objects, there is a force upon each of the objects. When the interaction ceases, the two objects no longer experience the force. Forces only exist as a result of an interaction. The direction towards which the force is applied is known as the direction of the force, and the application of force is the point where force is applied. For example, a force is applied by the wind when it propels a sailboat through the water, a force is also present when gravity pulls an apple downward. Things can move, change their speed, or change shape in response to forces. A force can cause an item to move from rest to motion or vice versa. Two or more things must interact with each other for a force to be created. For force to exist, there must be an interaction between at least two objects. This interaction between the objects may or may not be physical. Pulling a rope or hitting a ball with a bat come physical interaction whereas forces like the magnetic force, electrostatic force, etc come under non-physical force.

Pressure

Pressure has a direct relationship with force. Assuming that the area is constant, pressure increases as the force applied also increases. Pressure is defined as the physical force exerted on an object. The force applied is perpendicular to the surface of objects per unit area.

$$Pressure = \frac{Force}{Area} = \frac{F}{A}$$

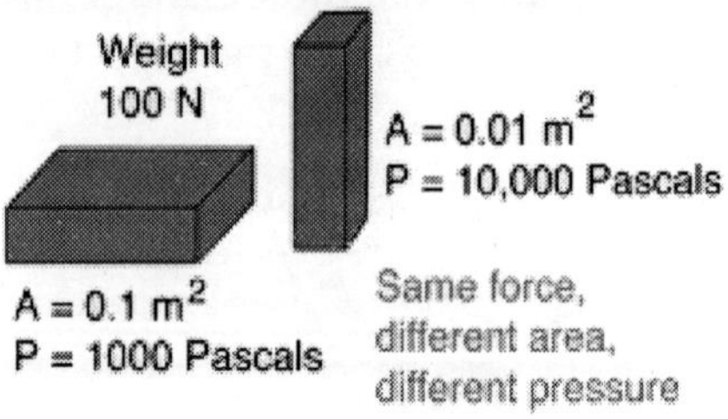

The basic formula for pressure is F/A (Force per unit area). Unit of pressure is Pascal's (Pa). Types of Pressures are Absolute, Atmospheric, Differential, and Gauge Pressure. The force applied perpendicular to the surface of an object per unit area over which that force is distributed is known as pressure. A simple example of pressure may be seen by holding a knife to a piece of fruit. If you hold the flat part of the knife against the fruit, it won't cut the surface. The force is spread out of a large area (low pressure). If you turn the blade so the cutting edge is pressed into the fruit, the same force is applied over a much smaller surface area (vastly increased pressure), so the surface cuts easily. A heavy chair, for example, exerts larger pressure on the floor than an empty box of the same surface area. On the other hand, pressure has an inverse relationship with area. As area increases, pressure decreases at a constant force.

Gravity

Gravity definition is analysed by the velocity of that freely falling object. The greater the masses of the objects, the greater the force. The force due to gravity is also stronger when objects are closer together. Every object that has mass exerts a gravitational pull or force on every other mass. The strength of this pull depends on the masses of objects at play.

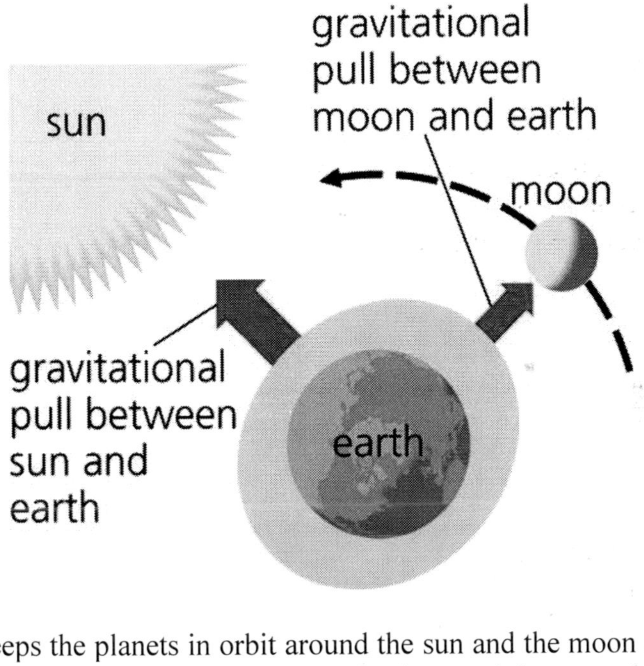

Gravity keeps the planets in orbit around the sun and the moon around the Earth. Gravity is one of the universe's fundamental forces and dominates every moment of our conscious experience. It keeps us close to the ground, drags baseballs and basketballs out of the air and gives our muscles something to struggle against. Gravity is the force by which a planet or other body draws objects toward its center. The force of gravity keeps all of the planets in orbit around the sun. For any two objects with some mass, the force of gravity has a tendency to attract them towards each other. This fact is according to the Universal Law of Gravitation. It is what causes the objects to have weight on the earth. When we weigh ourselves, the scale tells us how much gravity is acting on our bodies. All bodies on Earth have their particular weight or mass, or falling gravity force, directly proportional to their weight or mass, which is exerted by the Earth's mass. Certainly gravity is a force that exists between the Earth and the objects that are near it. As you stand upon the Earth, you experience this force. We have become accustomed to calling it the force of gravity. Gravity is also popular as gravitation. It is the force that occurs among all material objects in the universe.

Friction

Frictional force is the force generated by two surfaces that contact and slide against each other. These forces are mainly affected by the surface texture and the amount of force impelling them together. The angle and position of the object affect the amount of frictional force.

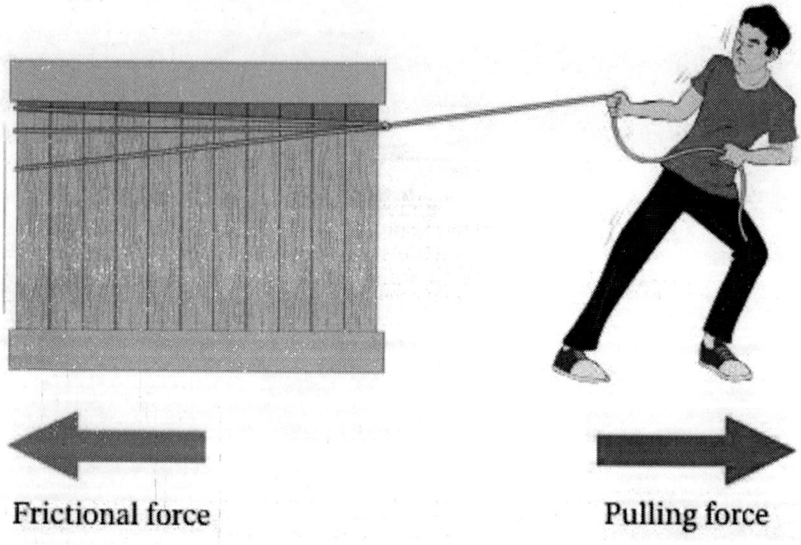

If an object is placed flat against an object, then the frictional force will be equal to the object's weight. Frictional Force is the opposing force when two surfaces come in contact with each other to move either in the same direction or in opposite directions. As friction is a force that opposes or resisted the motion of an object that comes in contact and slides against each other. Hence, the frictional force is a Contact Force. Friction is a force that always opposes motion. Static friction occurs when two surfaces are at rest with regard to one another. The value of static friction ranges from zero to the minimum force required to initiate motion. The force needed to initiate motion or to overcome static friction is always greater than the force needed to maintain motion or to overcome kinetic friction. Examples of friction can be found almost anywhere. A person walking down the street will experience friction as their shoes slide against the ground, and air resistance as they walk. They will also see friction happening as cars drive past them. The car's tires and engine are experiencing rolling friction as they travel.

Work

Work is said to be done when a force (push or pull) applied to an object causes a displacement of the object. We define the capacity to do the work as energy. Power is the work done per unit of time. The work done by a force on an object can be positive, negative, or zero, depending upon the direction of displacement of the object with respect to the force. For an object moving in the opposite direction to the direction of force, such as friction acting on an object moving in the forward direction, the work is done due to the force of friction is negative.

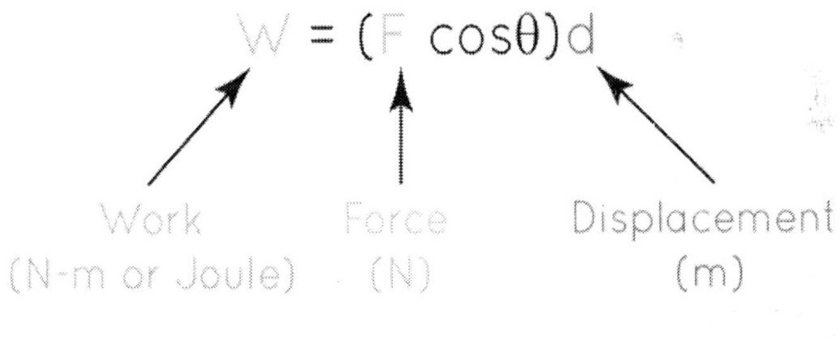

In the sense that a person who is feeling very enthusiastic is capable of doing a lot of work, energy is normally correlated with work completed. In this way, energy is characterised as the ability to perform work. We are doing work when we push or pull a heavy load or raise it off the floor, but a man carrying a heavy load and standing still is not doing work according to the scientific concept of work. Energy is another word we commonly use. Formally, the work done on a system by a constant force is defined to be the product of the component of the force in the direction of motion times the distance through which the force acts.

Power

Power can also be defined as the quantity of force required to cause a unit displacement. Power is a scalar quantity and is denoted by P. The average power is simply the average of the power values over a given period of time. This can be useful in situations where the power output is not constant, such as when starting or stopping a car. Power is the rate of doing an activity or work in the minimum possible time. It is the amount of energy transferred or converted per unit time where large power means a large amount of work or energy. Power is always dependent on work done, so if a person does work at different rates his power also differs at different times. Power is defined as the rate at which work is done upon an object. Power is a time-based quantity. Which is related to how fast a job is done. To calculate the average power, simply divide the total work done by the total time it took to do that work. When a force is applied to move an object, work is done on the object. Power can be thought of in a number of different situations. Some situations where power can be calculated are a car driving, a person running, and a horse pulling a cart.

Torque and Parabolic Path

Torque is effect of force when it is applied to an object containing a pivot point or the axis of rotation, which results in the form of rotational motion of the object. The Force causes objects to accelerate in the linear direction in which the force is applied, but in the case of torque, it causes objects to accelerate in the angular direction with respect to the axis of rotation. Torque is also called the "moment of force," as it depends on the magnitude of the force as well as the moment of the arm, i.e., the perpendicular distance between the line of action force and the axis of rotation. Torque is a measure of the force that can cause an object to rotate about an axis. Just as force is what causes an object to accelerate in linear kinematics, torque is what causes an object to acquire angular acceleration. Torque is a counterpart of force in rotational mechanics. The basic difference between them is that torque is the ability of a force to produce a twist around an axis. Torque is defined as the product of force and the perpendicular distance between the point of application of force and the pivot point. Torque in an electric medium means force experienced in an electric field. Similarly, torque in a magnetic medium is the force experienced in a magnetic field. These different velocities can be described as the x (horizontal) and y (vertical) components. Each of these components make up a pathway called a parabolic path. The shape of this path resembles that of an arch, rainbow, bridge, or water coming from a drinking fountain. For parabolic motion the accretion always points 'down'. For circular motion the acceleration always points toward the center of the circle. Both circles and parabolas are 'conic sections'. The other conic sections are ellipses and hyperbolas.

UNIT-IV
Motion and Levers

Newton's Laws of Motion and their implication in sports

Newton's laws of motion imply the relationship between an object's motion and the forces acting on it. In the first law, we understand that an object will not change its motion unless a force acts on it.

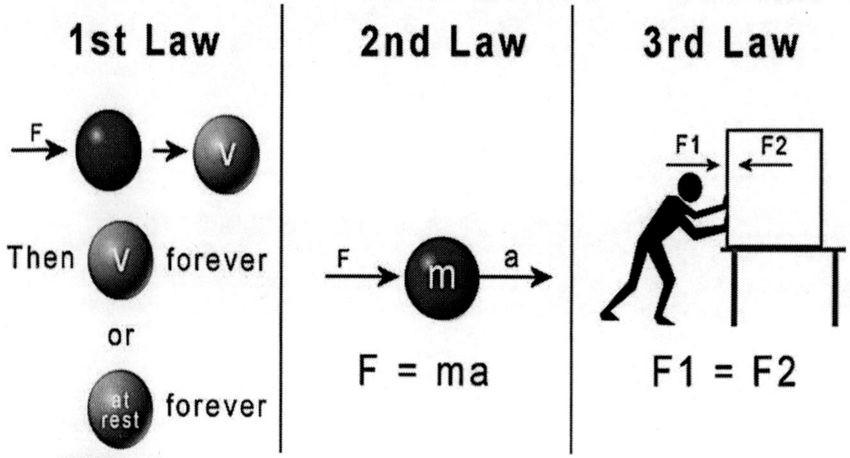

The second law states that the force on an object is equal to its mass times its acceleration. And finally, the third law states that there is an equal and opposite reaction for every action. Newton's laws are essential because they relate to everything we do or see in everyday life. These laws tell us how things move or stay still and why we don't float out of our bed or fall through the floor of our house. Newton's laws of motion are fundamental rules for understanding the motion of objects. There are three such Newton's laws. Each can be described in words and written as mathematical formulas that can be applied to problem-solving.

Newton's First Law of Motion Law of inertia –
This law states that a body at rest will remain at rest and a body in motion will remain in motion at the same speed and in the same direction till any external force is applied on it to change that state.

Application in Sports
In basketball, players on the court must keep in mind about dribbling because the ball will continue to bounce for some time if they lose control. If the ball bounces too far away from the player, his or her team can lose possession.

Newton's Second Law of Motion
This law states that the acceleration of an object is directly proportional to the force producing it and inversely proportional to its mass.

Application in sports
- Runners struggle while stopping at the finish line because it requires a very sudden change in motion.
- Shot-put throw.

Newton's Third Law of Motion
This law states that to every action, there is always an equal and opposite reaction.

Application in sports
- While swimming, the swimmer pushes the water backwards using his hands and thus attains a forward push due to an equal and opposite reaction from the water.

Mechanical Levers and their Implication in sports and physical education

A lever is a simple machine made of a rigid beam and a fulcrum. The effort (input force) and load (output force) are applied to either end of the beam. The fulcrum is the point on which the beam pivots. When an effort is applied to one end of the lever, a load is applied at the other end of the lever. This will move a mass upward. Levers rely on torque for their operation. Torque is the amount of force required to cause an object to rotate around its axis (or pivot point). Good examples of levers include the seesaw, crowbar, fishing line, oars, wheelbarrows, and the garden shovel. It is one of the six simple machines identified by Renaissance scientists. A lever amplifies an input force to provide a greater output force, which is said to provide leverage. A lever amplifies an input force to provide a greater output force, which is said to provide leverage. It is perfect for lifting or moving heavy things. It is a useful simple machine, and you can find them everywhere. Levers are the most basic machines which are used to do some work with minimal effort.

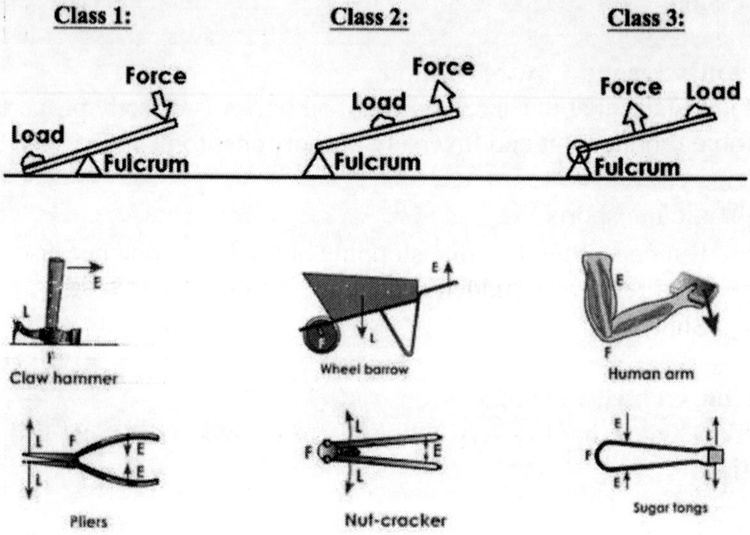

A lever is a rigid body that is capable of rotating at a point on itself. On the basis of the fulcrum's location, load, and effort, the lever is divided into a number of three types.

S.no	Types of Lever	Mechanical Advantage	Attribute
1.	First-class lever	Greater than 1	Force multiplier
2.	Second-class lever	Less than 1	Speed multiplier
3.	Third-class lever	Equal to 1	Change in direction of the effort

The ratio of the output force to the input force is the mechanical advantage of the lever. Many everyday tools use levers and fulcrums in their use, such as nail clippers, pliers, scissors, wheelbarrows, fishing rods, crow bars, and nutcrackers, just to name a few. The principles behind levers can also be explored by seeing how hard of a push is needed to open a door at different distances from its hinges. Also, leverage is a mechanical advantage gained in a system.

Implication in Sports and Physical Education

A lever amplifies an input force to provide a greater output force, which is said to provide leverage. The ratio of the output force to the input force is the mechanical advantage of the lever. Anatomical leverage system can be used to gain a mechanical advantage. Improve simple or complex physical movements. A lever system is a rigid bar that moves on a fixed point called the fulcrum when a force is applied to it. Movement is made possible in the human body by lever systems that are formed by our muscles and joints working together. An understanding of the levers in the body helps us to understand how movement is possible.

Meaning and concept of Equilibrium

When a body is in equilibrium, it stays in that position as long as there is no external influence on it. Equilibrium is a state of body where neither the internal energy nor the motion of the body changes with respect to time. The state of equilibrium occurs when all of the forces acting on the body are balanced by equal and opposite forces, resulting in the sum of the forces equaling zero.

However, a state of equilibrium does not mean that no forces act on the body but only that the forces are balanced. When no force is acting to make a body move in a line the body is in translational equilibrium, when no force is acting to make the body turn the body is in rotational equilibrium. When a body or a system is in equilibrium there is no net tendency to change. In mechanics, equilibrium has to do with the forces acting on a body.

Static equilibrium

A state of equilibrium in which the net external force and torque acting on a system is zero.

Dynamic equilibrium

A state of equilibrium in which the net external force and torque on a system moving with constant velocity are zero.

Centre of Gravity

The center of gravity is a point in an object where the distribution of weight is equal in all directions, and it does depend on the gravitational field. Center of gravity of an object is the point at which the mass or weight of the object is assumed to be concentrated. The center of gravity can be determined by taking the ratio of the summation of the product of the weight and the distance to the summation of the weights. Thus, the center of gravity of an object is defined as a point at which the whole mass or weight of the object is assumed to be concentrated. The best example for the center of gravity is the weighing balance and a seesaw in a children's park.

Theory Course

Course Code: PED307TH

Methods of Teaching in Physical Education

UNIT-I

Introduction

Meaning of Methods of Teaching

Teaching methods are techniques that educators can use to facilitate the teaching process and help students feel engaged and interested in the material. Teaching methods are ways to instruct students in a classroom, helping them to understand and remember what they've learned. Some of the best teaching strategies allow educators to convey information in a clear and concise way while also ensuring students retain it over the long term. If students can comprehend facts on a deep level and practice skills properly in the classroom, they can apply that wisdom and those abilities to their personal lives and their future careers.

Importance of Methods of Teaching in Physical Education

Teaching methods are the broader techniques used to help students achieve learning outcomes, while activities are the different ways of implementing these methods. Teaching methods help students:

- Master the content of the course.
- Learn how to apply the content in particular contexts.

Instructors should identify which teaching methods will properly support a particular learning outcome. Its effectiveness depends on this alignment. To make the most appropriate choice, an instructor should consider learning outcomes, student needs and the learning environment.

Principles of Teaching Methods

- Encourage contact between students and faculty.
- Develop reciprocity and cooperation among students.
- Encourage active learning.
- Give prompt feedback.
- Emphasize time on task.
- Communicate high expectations.
- Respect diverse talents and ways of learning.

Different Methods of Teaching

Command Method

The Command Method emphasizes direct and explicit instructions given by the teacher, focusing on demonstrating and modelling specific skills and techniques. It often involves a structured and teacher-centered approach, where students follow instructions and perform tasks accordingly. The command teaching style, also known as the authoritarian teaching style, involves the teacher providing a clear structure for the lesson and giving specific commands to students. This style is often used in physical education because it allows the teacher to establish a safe and efficient learning environment. By giving clear instructions and expectations, the teacher can ensure that students understand what they need to do and how to do it safely.

Lecture Method

Lecture method is teacher controlled and information centered approach in which teacher works as a role resource in classroom instruction. In this method, the only teacher does the talking and the student is passive listens. This creates dullness in the classrooms as the interaction between the pupil and teacher ceases to occur. In the lecture method, the teacher presents the learning concepts to the students. Teachers learn different concepts beforehand and explain the concepts in a classroom.

Demonstration Method

The demonstration method in teaching involves giving a demo or performing a specific activity to help students understand theories and concepts. This method requires clear language and the ability to ask questions and involves students' active participation and props, such as charts. The demonstration method in teaching can be defined as giving a demo or performing a specific activity or concept. In other words, the demonstration method is a teaching-learning process carried out in a very systematic manner. Demonstration often occurs when students have a difficult time connecting theories to actual practice or when students are unable to understand the application of theories.The demonstration teaching method may be effective in certain situations but is only suitable for some students and subjects.

Project Method

The project method is based on learning by doing. In this method, knowledge is given to the students directly through practical work. They get the chance to gain first-hand experience on the field, so they retain the learning for a longer period of time. The project method is psychological in nature, as the students are not just passive listeners but active participants. The project method of teaching is a medium of instruction in which the students are given a number of projects or situations out of which they have to choose the problem they want to solve. After the student has chosen the problem they want to solve, they will have to come up with a solution to the problem on their own. In the project method of teaching, the teacher is a guide and the activities carried out in the class are carried out by the students themselves. This helps improve self-reliance and self-responsibility among students. It helps students learn on their own and develop their own style of learning.

Reciprocal Method

Reciprocal Teaching is a great way to teach students how to determine important ideas from a reading while discussing vocabulary, developing ideas and questions, and summarizing information. Reciprocal teaching is a method in which a teacher gives students increased responsibility in the teaching process. A teacher first explains the key elements of assessing a piece of reading material and then shows how to use them. Once students are comfortable, the teacher allows the students to each assume control over an element and lead discussions for that phase. This allows the students to learn by doing.

Discussion Method

Discussion is important to learning in all disciplines because it helps student's process information rather than simply receive it. Leading a discussion requires skills different from lecturing. The goal of a discussion is to get students to practice thinking about the course material. In teaching, the discussion method is an instructional approach that promotes active student participation and engagement through dialogue and the exchange of ideas. The discussion method, as opposed to a teacher-centered lecture format, entails facilitating meaningful discussions among students and between the teacher and students. It develops critical thinking skills, problem-solving abilities, and the ability to articulate and defend one's ideas.

Individual Method

Individualized teaching makes learning stress-free and tailored. The environment encourages students to make mistakes and overcome their fears. The teacher reinforces their skills. Individualized instruction refers to educators using specific strategies, resources and assessments that cater to the needs of learners in their class. This process ensures that students are given guidance and flexibility in their learning process, enhancing their academic growth along the way.

Guided Method

Guided practice is important for students because it allows thinking about the new topic on their own. It allows the students to practice with a safety net. The students know the teacher is ready to help at any point. It also builds confidence. The guided discovery teaching style is based on the idea that students learn through exploration and inquiry. This approach requires the teacher to plan a series of questions and tasks that direct students towards discovering a pre-determined answer to the problem or learning target. Therefore, students must ask questions, explore new ideas, and experiment with different strategies to solve problems.

Problem Solving Method

The problem-solving method encourages students to actively participate in their own learning by engaging them in real-world problems that require critical thinking and collaboration. Problem-solving requires students to work together to find solutions. This promotes teamwork, communication, and cooperation. The problem-solving method helps students develop critical thinking skills by providing them with opportunities to analyse and evaluate problems. When students are engaged in solving real-world problems, they are more motivated to learn and apply their knowledge. The problem-solving method encourages students to be creative in finding solutions to problems. The problem-solving method of teaching often involves students working together to solve problems. This collaborative learning process helps students to develop their teamwork skills and to learn from each other. Problem-solving examples help students solve problems, which can build their confidence and strengthen their personalities. Students who master problem-solving methods can better express themselves and build confidence in their thinking ability. It helps connect them with their ideas and allows them to share them.

Co-operative Method

Cooperative learning involves students working together in small groups to accomplish shared goals or complete group tasks. It is widely recognised as a teaching strategy that promotes socialisation and learning among students from pre-school through to tertiary level and across different subjects and curriculum areas. Cooperative learning, also called small-group learning, is one teaching method that can help students learn academic material and social skills. Understanding more about cooperative learning can help you create a positive social experience in your classroom.

Inductive Method

The inductive method of teaching is a student-centric approach based on the idea that students are more likely to learn when they are actively engaged in the learning process. This approach challenges students to formulate their own beliefs or concepts by examining all the evidence provided and recognizing patterns to arrive at solutions. Educators often use it to help nurture children's inquisitive nature and foster creativity and group problem-solving. The inductive method of teaching through examples can aid students in remembering information by actually engaging the brain. After considering facts, figures, and other types of data, students have a stronger connection to the subject they are studying. Making mistakes might really help facts stick in your memory.

Deductive Method

The deductive model of teaching is more explanatory than based on discovery. Teachers have the responsibility of explaining the rules before the learners can dig into the whole thing. It may be the case that the learners find it hard to retain the focus throughout the class time. On the other hand, the inductive one is based firmly on discovery and figuring things out. Something to do individually or in a group should spike their interest a fair bit. Teachers can set the treasure hunt in motion and be the most silent spectator throughout the process. It begins by providing rules to learners along with examples, which are followed by specific activities, so that they can practice.

Factors Affecting Teaching Methods

Knowledge of the learners

The prior knowledge level of the learners is also quite vital in this teaching-learning process, as the teacher is supposed to deal with the pupils accordingly. The teacher is supposed to establish a link among the learners' existing knowledge and the novel knowledge they gain through the teaching-learning process.

Learning environment

Learning environment is where a student learns and a teacher teaches. The classroom environment is the learning environment for students which play an important role in the learning process. Both students and teachers get affected by the classroom environment. The environment for the learning is well maintained by active participation in education, concentration of students, teachers' focus on behavior of students etc. The environment of learning must be positive.

Teaching Skills

Now, there are multiple skills that the teacher is expected to possess, such as explanatory skills, presentation skills, communication skills, behavioural skills, etc., all of which have a huge impact on the way the content is delivered to the learners and also affects the quality of content. Good teaching skills help the learners to remain focused on what is being taught and help them understand better.

Instructional facilities

With the available teaching aids, teachers can cover a wide area of learning. It has many benefits such as differentiating instruction, relieving anxiety, helping learners to improve reading comprehension skills, illustrating or reinforcing a skill, presenting information in an effective way.

Educational Qualifications

Every teacher teaching a particular subject needs to have a minimum level of qualification for delivering the session as per the set norms and standards followed by the education board. This ensures that the quality of the subject matter is not compromised and that a knowledgeable person is teaching the respective pupils.

Lesson Planning

A lesson plan is the instructor's road map of what students need to learn and how it will be done effectively during the class time. Before you plan your lesson, you will first need to identify the learning objectives for the class meeting. Then, you can design appropriate learning activities and develop strategies to obtain feedback on student learning. A lesson plan provides you with a general outline of your teaching goals, learning objectives, and means to accomplish them, and is by no means exhaustive. A productive lesson is not one in which everything goes exactly as planned, but one in which both students and instructor learn from each other. Lesson plans help teachers be more effective in the classroom by providing a detailed outline to follow each class period.

Objectives of Lesson Plan

- Lesson plans provide a complete picture of all the learning taking place in a classroom and a quick reference of previous learning, making them an ideal resource for teachers to share with administrators and supervisors who require a real-time view of classroom progress.
- Learning objectives are often differentiated depending on the ability levels of students, and they should be such that children can see what they need to do to progress.
- Ideally, a learning objective should be something that children didn't know before the start of the lesson. That way, teachers can avoid any repetition in their classes. They should also look to continue from the work done in the previous lesson, and end where the next one is due to begin. Because of this, some teachers like to use planning overviews to help them organise their learning objectives.
- Lesson plan objectives refer to thorough descriptions of what your students should accomplish during a class.
- The planning allows teachers to double-check their understanding of the concepts being taught and ensure that they've gathered all materials to teach those concepts ahead of time, effectively passing that knowledge on to their students. It encourages greater student interaction and participation in the class.

Types of Lesson Plan

Daily Lesson Plan

Some teachers create lesson plans for each day of the week. The duration of each plan is the length of one class period or school day, so a teacher might create five lessons per week. Each day has a separate objective and a small assessment at the end to check for students' understanding of the day's content.

Weekly Lesson Plan

Weekly lesson plans consist of one lesson created to last for the entire week. This type of plan takes five consecutive class periods to complete. Educators teach the content earlier in the week, students practice using the content on their own midweek and then teachers assess students' understanding at the end.

A Whole Unit Lesson Plan

This lesson plan is ideal for teachers who prefer to teach their lessons from a per-unit perspective. You can customize your pace of teaching for each class depending on how well the students grasp each concept before moving on to the next topic in the unit.

Subject Specific Lesson Plan

If you are teaching multiple subjects in a single shift, you need to use a different lesson plan for each subject. Differentiating your planning can help achieve your targets and cover each of your lessons while avoiding confusion and maintaining focus when handling different topics.

Grade level Lesson Plan

In secondary classrooms, typically grades six to 12, some educators teach more than one grade level. Those teachers create different lesson plans depending on what grade level they're teaching each period. In the morning, a teacher may teach all sixth-grade science classes, and after lunch, they may have eighth-grade science for the rest of the day. They make specific plans because each grade level is learning different content at varying levels of depth.

Principles of Lesson Plan

Active Learner Engagement

Engaging learners actively in the learning process fosters deeper understanding and knowledge retention. Lesson planning empowers instructors to incorporate various interactive activities, such as group discussions, hands-on exercises, case studies, and problem-solving tasks. These activities encourage learners to participate actively, collaborate with peers, and apply their knowledge to real-life scenarios.

Lesson Topic

The lesson should begin with a topic derived from the adopted standards-based curriculum for a school or district. Because it relates to specific information the teacher is trying to impart, the topic should be part of the larger curriculum (such as unit instruction) required at your grade level.

Generalizing

This concept is concerned with the systematizing of the knowledge learned. Comparison and contrast lead to generalization. An effort should be made to ensure that students draw the conclusions themselves. It should result in students' own thinking, reflection and experience.

Assessment Alignment

Effective lesson planning includes aligning assessments with learning objectives. Instructors can design assessments that gauge learners' understanding, skills, and progress towards the desired outcomes. Well-aligned assessments ensure that learners are evaluated based on what they have learned and provide valuable feedback for both instructors and learners. By aligning assessments with lesson objectives, instructors can accurately measure learner achievement and identify areas that may require additional support.

Materials

This section lists any materials the students and teacher might use to complete the lesson successfully. Typical materials include specific pages from textbooks, printouts, writing utensils and paper. Listing materials in your lesson plan allows you to better prepare for the needs of your classroom.

Values of Lesson Plan

Builds the Confidence in Teachers
With a lesson plan in your hand, you will become a confident teacher. You would stay abreast with the novel teaching styles that are currently in vogue. You will not be following the principles of the old school of thought but will incorporate new teaching mechanisms. A lesson plan helps you adhere to the best teaching practices that deliver effective teaching. You will be come to be known as a confident teacher who is well-informed and highly knowledgeable faculty.

Classroom Management
Building the lesson plan outward from your learning goals also offers much-needed flexibility in adapting instructional delivery and classroom management during uncertain times. Classes that move from onsite to online or hybrid require different delivery methods, requiring adjustments to existing plans. Such situations highlight the importance of lesson planning in keeping the class moving smoothly from task to task regardless of the learning environment. Advance lesson planning also minimizes the need for discipline and allows you to make the most of your time with students.

Encouraging active learning and engagement
Well-designed lesson plans incorporate various teaching methods and activities that encourage active learning and engagement. This may include group discussions, hands-on exercises, case studies, or role-plays. By incorporating diverse learning activities, trainers can cater to different learning styles, improve knowledge retention, and promote a deeper understanding.

Student Assessment
The lesson plan translates the curriculum into clear daily goals for student learning that include a description of the objective and a way to measure the student's attainment of it. A few standard measurement methods are tests, homework assignments and group work. One benefit of the lesson plan is fitting the assessment to the particular goal while accounting for your specific situation. Some educational writers argue that teachers should design the evaluation before designing the learning activities.

Drive Teacher Success

Lesson planning requires a huge preparation and in-depth analysis of reviewing your teaching methodology. A well-documented lesson is a way to your career growth. Preparing lesson plans and evaluating them is the basic foundation for a teacher's success.

Evaluation

It allows the teachers to evaluate the performance and performance of individual students to identify their weaknesses, learn about their strengths, and provide feedback. It also helps develop an effective teaching strategy that focuses on different skills and abilities needed by students at each stage of their learning process link.

Motivation

A lesson Plan helps motivate the teachers and students to develop a lesson that appeals to various emotions and interests. The plan provides a detailed guide to follow when preparing for classes, which helps in motivating the students toward learning. It also encourages students to learn more about the topic by providing them with one step further into their learning process.

Class Activity/Recreational Part

Classroom activities play a vital role in a student's life. It offers to teach through various tasks assigned in the classrooms. Every activity aims at providing students with opportunities to deepen their learning. It improves their high-order thinking skills. They can learn the art of applying the concepts while articulating new knowledge and skills.

Assembly

School assembly is an important gathering in schools, bringing together students, teachers, and staff members. They gather for prayer and some activities like speech and reading. Morning assemblies in schools are held so that students and teachers start their day with positivity.

Revision

Revision is the process of reviewing and studying previously learned material to reinforce understanding and improve retention. It involves going over class notes, textbooks, and study materials to review key concepts, formulas, and examples. It is crucial for consolidating knowledge and enhancing long-term retention.

Reassembly

In a school, assembly is a gathering of all the teachers and pupils at the beginning of the school day.

Dismissal

If the whole class is ready, then you could dismiss students by birthday month, number of syllables in there first name, number of siblings, first letter of their name, student number, etc.

UNIT-II

Teaching Aids

Meaning of Teaching Aids

Teaching aids are any aiding objects, technology, or tools used in the teaching process by the teacher to make the class more interesting and effective. There are several teaching aids that can help in a classroom, such as visual aids, audio aids, audio-visual aids, etc. These tools aid the process of teaching and learning. Teaching aids could be like videos, working models, presentations, etc. These aids help the teachers to draw attention to the idea being taught in the class and also retain the information delivered for a longer duration of time. Teaching aids facilitate the learning of students in various ways. Teachers use different teaching aids to make their students listen attentively and interestingly. The traditional teaching aids involve the usage of blackboards, posters, globes, charts, textbooks, etc. However, as technology grows, teaching aids have also improved a lot, and today's teaching aids are classified into audio aids, visual aids, mechanical teaching aids, audio-visual aids, and more.

Importance of Teaching Aids in Physical Education

Enhances their Thinking Skills

Utilizing various teaching aids can help you in developing thinking skills of your students. Rather than assuming something in the mind, the students can see and comprehend how an experiment is being conducted, for instance. They can understand everything clearly and think of implementing concepts practically. When they start thinking practically, they will eventually develop their thinking and creative skills.

Help in Memorizing Concepts

Students who easily forget the lesson's teachings will benefit the most from the use of teaching aids. When they are taught through these aids, you not only define the concept orally but also utilize practical methods like models, graphs, etc., to help students understand the concept better. Therefore, they tend to retain all this information for longer periods if they learn the topics in an interactive way.

Helps to Remember Concepts
Students who tend to forget the concepts easily will benefit from the usage of teaching aids. When teaching aids are used, teachers not only define everything orally, but they use practical methods to make students understand better, such as models, graphs, etc. Teaching aids also make learning more interesting, and students tend to remember the concepts longer if they learn them with interest.

Support Inclusive Education
Teaching aids can enhance inclusivity in the classroom by accommodating diverse needs and abilities. For instance, learners with visual impairments can benefit from tactile or auditory aids, while students with hearing impairments may benefit from visual aids or captions. By using teaching aids that cater to different abilities, educators can create an inclusive learning environment where all students can thrive.

Develop motor skills
Teaching aids help to develop motor skills in the students as they actively participate in classroom activities. They come to know how to use and maintain different types of teaching aids.

Easier to Teach Complex Concepts
Students skip certain topics that they find difficult to comprehend and learn. Such complex concepts can be easily taught using any of the teaching aids like visual ones. This will help students in comprehending complex concepts easily and in an interactive way.

Provide experience
Teaching aids give direct experience to students and provide complete practical picture of the concept to the students. Thus students grasp the concepts easily when they are taught with specific teaching aids.

Complex Concepts Become Easier To Learn
Students sometimes skip topics that are harder to understand and learn. No matter how many times they study, some topics may feel complicated for them. Such topics can be easily taught using the appropriate teaching aids. Teaching aids help them to understand complex concepts in a faster way, and they no longer skip topics from studying.

Application of Knowledge
The goal of teaching tools is frequently to close the knowledge gap between theory and application. Students may observe how the ideas they learn in the classroom are applicable to their surroundings through real-life examples and simulations.

Reinforcing a Skill or Concept
Teaching aids prove to be a formidable supplement for teachers when the reinforcement of a skill or concept is necessary. Not only do they allow students more time to practice, but they also present the information in a way which offers students a different way to engage with the material. Of course, this is important in order to reach the various learning types in the class.

Active Engagement
By grabbing students' attention and motivating them to participate in the learning process, teaching aids promote active engagement. Students are more likely to retain material and refine their critical thinking abilities when they are actively involved.

Types of Teaching Aids

Audio Aids

Audio aids help a lot in learning languages where communication and listening are important. Auditory learning makes the students develop their listening skills. It may involve playing a paragraph in audio, making your students listen to it and answer your questions, or playing some calm music in your classroom to make your students feel relieved and more. By listening to the radio, students can improve their listening and understanding skills.

Radio
Radio is an important instrument to foster the sense of unity and integrity among the people. The cultural programmes, debates, talks, through broadcasts involve a strong desire among the people to know each and other's culture and values. Radio allows students to learn at their own pace and convenience. They can tune in to educational programs at specific times

or access archived broadcasts later, allowing for greater flexibility in their learning schedules.

Tape-Recorder

An audio tape recorder, tape deck or tape machine is an audio storage device that records and plays back sounds, including articulated voices, usually using magnetic tape, either wound on a reel or in a cassette, for storage. Tape recorded can be used by a teacher intending to be absent from school due to some reasons. The lesson could be recorded and lesson arrangements made for the lessons to be replayed to the students during the time of absence.

Gramophone

Gramophone is an audio aid, it is used to play previously recorded sounds. Gramophone is a useful teaching device. It is possible to bring music, addresses, textual materials and instructional lessons into the classroom through gramophone just as effectively as it is possible through radio. This teaching aid is used for different purposes. It is useful for the teaching of music and language. The lingua phone records can be used to teach language correctly particularly good pronunciation and speech. Teacher should be careful at the time of using Gramophone. He must introduce the students regarding the subject matter contains in the records. Students are to listen it carefully and note down the intricacies of music or language there in.

Microphone

Microphones for teaching with good sound quality and easy operation are always important tools. It is all too common for students to not understand the teacher's words because the audio is not clear, and mishearing can lead to the wrong message being delivered. Microphones are a useful piece of audio equipment for schools and higher education facilities. When lecturers and teachers use a microphone, their voices can be more easily heard by their students. It helps to reduce the amount of effort that students have to spend concentrating to hear, allowing their concentration to be focused on understanding the study material. The risk of misunderstanding information or loss of information is also reduced.

Teleconferencing

Teleconferencing can be beneficial to professionals looking to work remotely or in separate geographical locations. With teleconferencing, educators can make themselves available even when they are not at the school. This means they can lecture students who might need their help outside office hours, or collaborate with other experts and specialists without them having to be in the same classroom. Teleconferencing is the use of a telecommunication device to communicate between two or more people.

Visual Aids

Visual aids are the kind of material that we can see with our eyes. It is the most important teaching aid that teachers always use in their teaching-learning process everyday like book, blackboard, chalk, duster, indicator, picture, map, graphs, charts, posters, bulletin boards, museums, projectors and also important visual aids. Showing student's visual images, such as maps, charts, graphs, photographs and pictures of people can help students get excited about a particular topic.

Blackboard

The blackboard is probably the simplest, cheapest, most convenient, and widely used non-projected visual aid in extension teaching. It is suitable for use in lectures, training programs, group meetings, etc. Blackboard should be kept clean so that writing on it could be easily read by the students from all parts of the room. Black board is also main tool in teaching. Board is where teacher give information of lesson.

Specimens

Specimens are inexpensive and can be easily collected from the same sources as objects. In some cases where original objects are not usable specimens can serve the purpose. Presentation of specimens in a class depends upon their size and the size of the group of students.

Posters

Posters help learners to focus on a certain idea, event, fact or process. Posters are a convenient way for both students and teachers to help students understand the topics a lot faster. Posters are an excellent tool for visual learners, who comprise a significant percentage of students. Using educational posters as a visual aid with other teaching materials, teachers can present information visually appealing and engagingly, making the learning process easier for students to comprehend and remember.

Overhead Projector

The overhead projector is use to effective teaching learning activity. Projectors can help teachers better meet the needs of their students by displaying information differently. Like with chalkboards and whiteboards, teachers can still provide visual aids to accompany their verbal points. However, they can also add images and videos, helping further clarify new or unfamiliar concepts across disciplines. An overhead projector is a very basic but reliable tool used to display images onto a screen or wall. It consists of a large box containing a cooling fan and an extremely bright light, with a long arm extended above it.

Epidiascope

Epidiascope is a projector capable of projecting images that are both transparent and opaque. Epidiascopes are projectors with an episcope and a diascope combined into their optical system. The epidiascope is a type of opaque projector developed in the early years of the 20th century. Unlike the episcope or epidioscope, which have the ability to project opaque images only, epidiascopes can project images of both transparent and opaque images. This quality made the device especially useful in educational circles for most of the century.

Maps

There are many uses of maps for students, but ultimately, map reading helps students improve problem-solving and reasoning skills. For example, students can calculate how far the library is from their school or house. They can also formulate the easiest and fastest routes to travel to favourite vacation spots. This builds students' self-sufficiency and confidence in their ability to formulate solutions.

Film Strips

Filmstrips were used to show educational films in classrooms, serving as a predecessor of videocassettes, DVDs and Blu-ray technology. Filmstrip projectors allowed teachers to show presentations for class discussions by turning a knob. So it helped and developed the imagination of students. It brought visual awakening to the system. A filmstrip projector is an instrument designed to accept 35 mm filmstrips. It is often equipped with an adapter to accept 2 x 2 slides. Models are available with manual advance and remote control.

Graphs

A graph is used in many subjects such as geography, history, mathematics, science, or also to explain climate. And graphs are used to give information about population etc. as well. Also, the graph is most commonly used in teaching mathematics and science. They are two-dimensional materials having no depth which communicate facts, ideas and relationships clearly through words, lines, drawings, symbols and pictures.

Globes

Globes facilitate the teaching and learning of key geographical concepts, including the identification of countries, capitals, major cities, mountain ranges, rivers, and other essential geographic features. They help students develop a solid foundation in global geography, enabling them to navigate and understand the world more effectively. Globes provide a valuable tool for contextualizing current events and understanding global issues.

Audio-Visual Aids

All such aids that endeavour to create things clear to us through our senses are referred to as "Audio-Visual Aids" or educational Materials. These learning materials create educational things as real as potential and provide us primary data through the organs of hearing and seeing. Audio-Visual aids give a complete learning atmosphere for students. It lets them experience practical experience from the comfort of the classroom. It makes learning more realistic and lively for students.

Television

Television in the classroom is a great help for younger students. It can help them find more interest and fun in learning. One reason schools should have televisions in each room, and a great satellite or cable package, is that it can be a great tool for teaching. The students are curious to attend the Television Period. It provides them both education and entertainment. The teacher finds even the dullest students taking interest in such discussions. Now the back benchers come forward to take front benches. It shows their increased confidence.

Computer

Computers can be used for online education & research. With the help of the internet, students can find useful information about their projects, assignments and also can take useful help from other researchers as they store & organize their research materials in computers. The use of computers is one of the most used tools in the modern education system. With the help of this electronic device, the education world has got a golden opportunity of learning. The use of computers can be seen not only in the education world but also in different areas of their life.

Sound Motion Films

The motion picture offers common denominator of experience. Reading opportunities differ with different students. But even illiterates can obtain ideas from films, and they will be able to discuss and share them with others. The motion picture is an edited version of reality. Heightening reality is the major function of the motion picture. Like a number of other audio-visual materials the motion picture can heighten reality and its three dimensional effect renders it the most effective tool of teaching.

Audio Video Tape

Video tapes were widely used for recording and playback of television programs and home movies before the advent of digital video technologies such as DVDs and digital video recorders (DVRs). Advantages of video tape include its ability to record and play back high-quality video and audio, its relatively low cost, and its durability. Video tape is a medium for storing audio and visual information. It consists of a long strip of plastic coated with magnetic material, on which the audio and visual information is recorded.

Chalk board

Writing information on a chalkboard helps teachers take visible cues from students. Teachers can immediately address students' body language and facial expressions that suggest confusion about the material. Teaching with chalk is especially an advantage for teachers of students with mixed learning abilities. A chalk board or blackboard is a surface that the teacher uses to explain concepts to students. They can write on this board with a stick made of calcium carbonate. Chalkboard is very useful to show solutions of the different mathematical problems systematically.

Charts

The chart is an effective and easy to use graphic organizer because of its simple and straightforward layout. Charts can have up to ten rows and ten columns, in any configuration the user would like depending on their needs. Charts or diagrams can help reinforce information that students are learning or have already learned. Hang the chart where students can see it. Ideally, the chart should be at the students' eye level or just above eye level. Use charts that have clear images and large text. Furthermore, the use of charts in teaching and learning is highly advised because it unfolds a whole lot of ideas that real life models may not unfold. There are also courses that require the use of instructional materials in the teaching and learning in order to enhance students understanding of the concept and to also clear any doubt and misconception the students may have.

Model

Model is a very important teaching aid for science and geography teaching. Model has a three-dimensional effect on the mind of the students. They are the replica of the real subject matter. Models and modelling play a crucial role in science practice. When the actual substance cannot be brought into the classroom or its size is so large or it is not available then teachers prepare its sample or model which is shown in the classroom so that the student can easily be explained. Teaching models provide direction to instructors and planners while also speeding up the educational process. It helps them to assess and improve on their strengths and weaknesses. When developing such models, teachers consider elements such as social, personal, information processing, and behavior.

Slide Projector

There are several different components to a slide projector, starting with a slot where slides can be inserted. Many slide projectors are designed to work with carousels, circular racks of slides which can be rotated to allow a sequential projection of images which may be automatic, or controlled with a button or remote operated by the user. Projectors enable teachers to create bulleted PowerPoint presentations or other highly organized notes for the class. With the use of projectors in the classroom, students can take better notes with the ability to discern what information the teacher displays is most useful to them. Slide projector is a small piece of transparent which is use to show the real things or images. It is a projected aid. In this slide projector generally 20-50 slides and about 1.5 meters long filmstrip.

Motion picture

The motion picture can be used to assist the pupils in their understanding of abstractions, in encouraging thinking, and thus leading them to further reflect on human relationships. Interest is an important factor of learning. On a general level, many students respond better to watching movies than to reading which helps in keeping them interested and prevent them from getting easily distracted. This is especially effective for those who are not motivated readers and prefer videos over the written word. The motion picture can control the time factor in any operation or series of events. Time control is excellent feature of the motion picture. It can show what happens when a cup of milk drops to the floor and it can speed up action so as to slow such a process as plant growth which, of course, occurs at rates too show for the human eyes.

Use and Improvisation of Apparatus

The use of improvised apparatus is an effective step taken towards reducing the cost in Integrated Science teaching. An improvised apparatus in science projects is an apparatus which is used as an alternative for the original equipment. There are lots of different types of apparatus. You can have sports equipment called apparatus, equipment for specific activities called apparatus, or scientific apparatus which you might find in a laboratory.

Presentation Technique

Presentation Techniques are all the essential skills you ought to develop to deliver presentations successfully and become a better presenter. Presentation techniques include focusing on the audience, cutting down to the core idea, brainstorming, using visual aids, the 10-20-30 rule, structuring, recording yourself, practice and feedback, and open body language. Presentation techniques helps to better communicate with others. By giving presentations, it allows you to tell others what you have recently done or what you have known. A presentation is a method of communicating information from a speaker to an audience. Presentations are usually demos, introductions, lectures, or speeches intended to enlighten, convince, inspire, motivate, develop goodwill, or introduce a new idea/product.

Criterion of Presentation Technique

Some of the criteria that you can use to assess presentations include:

- Focus of the presentation.
- Clarity and coherence of the content.
- Thoroughness of the ideas presented and the analysis.
- Clarity of the presentation.
- Effective use of facts, statistics and details.
- Lack of grammatical and spelling errors.
- Design of the slides.
- Effective use of images.
- Clarity of voice projection and appropriate volume.
- Completion of the presentation within the allotted time frame.

Qualities of Good Presenter

Know your topic well

It's important to be knowledgeable about your presentation topic so you will come across as confident. Thoroughly studying your topic will also help you feel more confident and offer helpful answers to audience questions after your presentation.

Keep slides and visual aids simple

Try to avoid using too much text on your slides. Slide presentations can be a great way to share information and structure your talking points but use them sparingly. Pictures, graphs and bullet points look cleaner than large blocks of text and prevent you from reading off the slides too much. Your deck should be visually appealing to keep your audience engaged.

Confidence

Build your confidence from the inside out by managing nervousness, and turning it to power. Build your confidence from the outside in by fine-tuning your delivery skills. Powerful stance, steady eye contact, a relaxed face; these are typically seen as confidence.

Calm

The best presenters have a sense of ease about them. You see it on their faces, in their gestures and body language, and in their words. They seem comfortable in their own skins. They don't rush. They allow pauses. They know what they are doing. That calms the audience. They have a sense of calm commitment that draws the audience in without screaming. Their calm is focused and somehow energized from within.

Good Eye Contact

One of the best ways to engage with your audience is through eye contact. When you make eye contact with someone, it shows that you're interested in what they have to say and that you're engaged in the conversation.

An Organized Structure

Another important presentation skill is having a well-organized structure. This means having an introduction, main body, and conclusion to your presentation. It also means using transitions between sections to help your audience follow along.

Factors Influencing Presentation Technique

Audience Analysis

When the speaker has made some background research about the audience in a proper manner, it results in excelling in the presentation. However, when the audience analysis is poor, it will result in an ineffective presentation.

Communication environment

The effectiveness of the presentation is highly influenced by the communication environment. Maximum people of the audience notice the surrounding. These surroundings include the speaker, stage, background, lighting, aeration and so forth. If the arrangements are not proper then it will have an adverse impact on the presentation.

Stage presence

During a presentation, projecting confidence can help keep your audience engaged. Stage presence can help you connect with your audience and encourage them to want to watch you.

Storytelling

Incorporating storytelling into a presentation is an effective strategy used by many powerful public speakers. It has the power to bring your subject to life and pique the audience's curiosity. Don't be afraid to tell a personal story, slowly building up suspense or adding a dramatic moment. And, of course, be sure to end with a positive takeaway to drive your point home.

Choosing the Right Visual Aids

Visual aids can be a powerful tool in any presentation, but it's important to choose the right ones. Consider using charts, graphs, images, or videos to help illustrate your message. Just be sure to keep your visuals simple and easy to understand.

UNIT-III

Introduction of Teaching Skills

Teaching Skills

Teaching skills are integral to the role of educators. These skills provide guidance in navigating daily classroom activities, enabling teachers to create an optimal learning environment that nurtures students' curiosity and eagerness to explore various subjects. Patience stands out as one of the most vital characteristics of an effective teacher. Each student is unique, influenced by factors such as age, prior education, personal circumstances, and individual needs. While teachers must adhere to certain timelines, they cannot expect every student to progress at the same pace. They must possess the patience and empathy to communicate with students individually, if necessary, and assist them in overcoming any challenges they encounter during their learning journey. If every student instantly grasped the concepts being taught, teaching would indeed be simpler, but far less fulfilling. The role of a teacher heavily relies on their organizational skills. Even when following a strict curriculum, teachers must know how to efficiently manage their time and accomplish their class objectives within the given timeframe. This includes preparing the necessary materials ahead of time, like scientific equipment and textbooks, to avoid wasting any time.

Lecture method

Lecture method is most convenient and inexpensive method of teaching any subject. It hardly requires the use of scientific apparatus, experiment, and aids materials except for the black board. Lecture method is teacher controlled and information centered approach in which teacher works as a role resource in classroom instruction. In this method, the only teacher does the talking and the student is passive listens. This creates dullness in the classrooms as the interaction between the pupil and teacher ceases to occur. This consistency guarantees that all students have an equal opportunity to understand the information and decreases the possibility of differences or misunderstandings caused by varying delivery or content. Lectures can be effective for conveying complex information and providing an overview of a topic. However, they may be most effective when used in combination with other teaching strategies that encourage active learning and interaction, such as group work, discussion, or hands-on activities.

Command method

The command style is characterized by instructing the students to produce a predicted response to a certain stimulus provided by the teacher. For example, the teacher may show how to serve a volleyball while the students follow the instructions. This is especially important because visual learning has proven to be the most common learning medium when it comes to learning a motor task. After demonstrating the skill, the teacher makes the students perform it at the same time according to a certain stimulus, such as blowing the whistle. The command teaching style, also known as the authoritarian teaching style, involves the teacher providing a clear structure for the lesson and giving specific commands to students. This style is often used in physical education because it allows the teacher to establish a safe and efficient learning environment.

Discussion method

The discussion method, as opposed to a teacher-centered lecture format, entails facilitating meaningful discussions among students and between the teacher and students. It develops critical thinking skills, problem-solving abilities, and the ability to articulate and defend one's ideas. Discussion-based instruction allows for both agreement and disagreement, and it is built on democratic principles. Since the teaching method is entirely discussion-based, if a student provides the right answer, he or she can share it with the teacher if the teacher makes a mistake in the classroom. Discussions incorporate characteristics of learner-centered instruction; learners are at the center of the learning process, teacher's guide learners, deep understanding of the topic is a goal, and social interaction is emphasized.

Project method

The project method of teaching is a medium of instruction in which the students are given a number of projects or situations out of which they have to choose the problem they want to solve. After the student has chosen the problem they want to solve, they will have to come up with a solution to the problem on their own. Project-based learning is an innovative and engaging approach to teaching that is gaining popularity in classrooms around the world. Instead of relying on traditional lectures and rote memorization, project-based learning immerses students in real-world, hands-on projects that require them to think critically, work collaboratively, and communicate effectively. In project method of teaching the role of a teacher is that of a guide, friend and philosopher not a dictator or commander.

Demonstration method

The demonstration method in teaching involves giving a demo or performing a specific activity to help students understand theories and concepts. This method requires clear language and the ability to ask questions and involves students' active participation and props, such as charts. The demonstration teaching method may be effective in certain situations but is only suitable for some students and subjects. For example, in matters that require critical thinking and problem solving, such as math and science, more than simply demonstrating a concept may be necessary for students to grasp the material fully. Some students may need help with active participation and feel uncomfortable asking questions in front of their peers.

Imitation method

Imitation is a crucial aspect of skill development, because it allows us to learn new things quickly and efficiently by watching those around us. Most children learn everything from gross motor movements, to speech, to interactive play skills by watching parents, caregivers, siblings, and peers perform these behaviors. Imitation is a pivotal skill for children with and without disabilities, serving both learning and social interaction functions for young children. Imitation training works in a building block method. Imitation of simple skills gets taught first. Then these imitations are combined to teach more sophisticated, advanced skills. Focusing on what the child already knows as a foundation approaches learning in a positive way rather than just emphasizing deficits. If the learner does not display the skill, the teacher provides a prompt to help bring out the skill in a learner, instead of taking the 'wait and see' approach.

UNIT-IV
Class Formation

Class Formation

Class Formation is a collaborative process for the placement of children into classes will lead to greater efficiency, increased understanding and improved opportunities for learning. Group formations in physical education are a means to carry out activities in groups of multiple members.

Values of Class Formation

- It is important for students' social and emotional development that they make and participate in healthy friendships at school. Learning to make new friends and interact effectively with all types of people is an important part of children's development.
- In 13 plus years of education, your child will eventually find themselves in a class without their close friends.

Types of Class Formation

- Oppositional Class Formation
- Repressive Class Formation

Supervision of Teaching Methods

Educational supervision is a term used to identify the work duties of administrative workers in education. Educational supervisors make sure the educational institution operates efficiently and within the legal requirements and rules. The purpose of this field is to make sure teachers and other faculty members are doing what they're supposed to be doing and that students are receiving the best education possible. Supervision can be defined as a creative and dynamic expert technical service to improve the overall teaching learning process in particular and overall education system in general. Educational supervision means an all-out effort of the school officials directed towards providing leadership to teachers and other educational workers for the improvement of institution. Supervision is incredibly important and should be planned for school staff at all levels, including leaders. Ensuring you receive regular, meaningful supervision can make all the difference, particularly when dealing with those cases where we still feel the weight of our shoulders when we get home and walk in the front door. Effective and constructive supervision should provide support, coaching opportunities and development training for staff working with children.

Inspection of Teaching Methods

Inspections encourage collaboration between teachers and the inspector on a professional level. During the inspection, the inspector spends the majority of his or her time engaging in direct observation of teaching and learning at the classroom level. Inspection is a mandatory process for every school or class, and it is sometimes done by the government or sometimes the head of the school as well. Moreover, school inspection provides policy and decision makers with accurate information about the current state of education in their respective institutions.

Methods of Supervision

The five types of supervision available in education are:-

1. Inspection
2. Absolute Freedom
3. Compulsion Type
4. Training and Direction
5. Democratic Leadership

Qualities of a Supervisor

Strong Verbal and Written Communication
For teams to function effectively, supervisors must have strong communication skills. This includes clearly articulating goals and expectations, as well as being able to share the needs of the team externally to other leaders. Both verbal and written abilities matter and include things like spelling, grammar, tone, and the ability to correctly convey ideas. Strong interpersonal communication skills can help the team thrive. These include things like frequent and authentic one-on-ones with employees,

ensuring workers understand how their role supports the company's goals, and providing transparency.

Strong Leadership

The supervisor should serve as an example to their staff. They must assert leadership and make their employees want to follow them as they take their organization through regular business changes. A strong leader will encourage their group, improve teamwork and lead the way to success.

Confidence and positivity

Your attitude and demeanor are contagious and can greatly influence the atmosphere in your workplace. Try to approach each day and situation with positivity and optimism. Also, focus on showing confidence both in yourself and your team. As much as possible, show passion for the company and its objectives and inspire your team members can share that excitement. Supervisors lead by example as often as they lead by command.

Critical Thinking

There are many tasks that a supervisor needs to deal with that require excellent critical thinking skills. With a high-level position comes more responsibilities and more decisions to be made. Critical thinking skills make the decision process more manageable.

Approachability and empathy

A good supervisor works closely with their team and should be easily accessible when questions, conflicts or issues arise. As a supervisor, you will need to listen when your employees come to you with workplace complaints or suggestions. This requires important social skills such as empathy and emotional intelligence (being aware of your own emotions as well as those of others).

Excellent Listener

Finally, good supervisors must be good listeners. While their job involves giving others direction, they need to be adept at drawing out others and listening carefully to their input so they can remove barriers and establish an environment that furthers organizational goals and leads to success. Supervisors play a role of resolving conflicts by listening carefully to different perspectives of employees. That listening involves empathy and the ability to truly understand the needs of co-workers and others.

Evaluation of Teaching Methods

Evaluation of teaching involves collecting evidence, from various stakeholders, for the purpose of improving the effectiveness of the teaching-learning process. A successful evaluation generates outcomes that are valid, reliable and indicate directions and action for development. The goal of evaluation is to provide teachers and students with information to improve learning outcomes and measure the effectiveness of teaching and learning practices. Evaluation methods can include tests, quizzes, essays, projects, observations, and more. Evaluation is an important aspect of the educational process as it helps teachers understand student learning and adjust their teaching practices accordingly. Learning the types of evaluation is an essential tool for individuals still learning, such as students of an educational institution. Without the skill of utilizing types of evaluation in education, it may be hard to see definitive progress in our student lives.

Need and Importance of Evaluation

To clarify the objectives of education
The importance of evaluation lies in clarifying the objectives of education. The main goal of education is to bring about a transformation in the learner's behavior. Through evaluation, teachers can provide evidence of this behavioural change.

It provides Guidance
If a teacher possesses adequate knowledge about their learners, they are able to provide guidance. However, this guidance can only be given after a thorough evaluation that considers all aspects such as abilities, aptitude, interest, and intelligence.

Helpful in classification
Evaluation is a valuable tool through which a teacher can gain insight into the diverse levels of intelligence, ability, and interest among their students. By utilizing this information, the teacher can effectively categorize their students and offer them appropriate guidance.

Helpful in Improvement of Teaching and Learning process

Through evaluation, a teacher has the opportunity to not only enhance the development of their students' personality and learning abilities, but also gain valuable insights into the effectiveness of their teaching methods and make necessary improvements. Consequently, evaluation plays a crucial role in enhancing the overall teaching and learning experience.

Diagnostic

The process of evaluation is ongoing and extensive, serving as a valuable tool for teachers to identify and address any issues or challenges faced by their students.

Remedial

When we refer to remedial work, we are discussing the appropriate course of action that a teacher can take in order to address identified issues and provide solutions that will result in a positive transformation in the learner's behavior and overall personal development.

Theory Course

Course Code: PED308TH

Officiating and Coaching

UNIT-I
Introduction

Introduction of Officiating

Officiating is an integral part of sports whether athletes find themselves at the introductory or professional level. Sports officiating requires hard work and dedication long before stepping on the field or court. Officiating affords an individual the opportunity to develop interpersonal skills and to hone one's judgment skills. Football officiating requires you to make instantaneous decisions, resolve conflicts, and deal with stress and pressure. It demands good communications skills and the ability to think on your feet. The ability to work a game fairly and smoothly is a skill one can be proud of. Some sports officials, such as boxing referees, may work independently. Others, such as baseball or softball umpires, work in groups. Each official working in a group may have different responsibilities. For example, in baseball, one umpire is responsible for signalling balls and strikes while others are responsible for signalling fair and foul balls out in the field.

Officials are an essential part of sport. They ensure that the game is played fairly, in accordance with the rules. Officiating can be fun, life-changing, contribute to leadership, personal development and is a practical strategy for the sport and recreation industry to encourage people in a non-playing role to stay involved in sport. Officials will determine and modify their styles as they become more experienced. Over time, they will get to understand how rival games are played, the magnitude of certain games and the varying levels of play between different leagues. A person's style of officiating is also enhanced by their ability to signal the right calls, interpret body language and communicate effectively during different situations.

Introduction of Coaching

Coaching and sport instruction are similar in many ways. Both are performed by professionals who have mastered knowledge about physical activities, as well as the skills and techniques required to transmit that knowledge to other people. Both also require expertise in designing practice experiences that stimulate learning and conditioning experiences to enhance performance. Sports coaches bring out ability by identifying needs and planning and implementing suitable training programmes. Whatever the context, coaching involves developing the participants physical and psychological fitness and providing the best possible practical conditions in order to maximise their performance. However, sport coaching jobs have many different components. While one of the main responsibilities of a sports coach is undoubtedly maximising standards of play, it can also involve discovering potential, creating training programmes, and inspiring youngsters or those from underrepresented backgrounds in sports.

Sports coaches must have strong communication skills in order to teach their athletes the rules of the game, proper techniques and advanced strategies. Communication skills are also critical for organizing and motivating the team and giving clear and precise directions in a way that the athletes can immediately understand and act upon. Sports coaches need to be able to motivate athletes on an individual basis and also organize them to help them win as a team. For this reason they need strong leadership skills like positivity, management skills and the ability to inspire others. Sports coaches train amateurs to compete in a sport – either individually or as a team. This can be invigorating as well as frustrating for the men and women on the side-lines.

Importance of Officiating in Games and Sports

Officials are responsible for their actions and attitudes.

There are a number of expectations of officials including:

- **Prepared for their role** - Prepared Physically and mentally for the Task.
- **Competent** - have and are further developing the skills for the task.
- **Trustworthy** - Honest and Impartial.
- **Responsible** - Have Integrity and Take the Role Seriously.

A really capable official is able to win confidence of players in no time. It is equally essential for the players to repose unquestioned faith in the official. Successful officiating is then of utmost importance in inculcating the spirit of the game and to raise the level of officiating. An official should face unusual circumstances during the course of the game. A capable official must face the circumstances with courage and without overstepping the rules or the code of ethics. An official is always above prejudices. It is important that officials present in a manner that portrays officiating in a positive and respected manner. Officials undertake an important role in the staging of competitions. Officials must be provided with a respectful, appreciative and supportive environment in which to undertake their role. Officials need to be appropriately recognised and rewarded for performing their role. The industry must remain flexible and inclusive in facilitating innovative strategies in the recruitment, development and retention of officials.

Importance of Coaching in Games and Sports

It builds confidence

A coach typically shares exercises and techniques for building up your self-esteem and self-confidence. Confidence can help employees feel comfortable accepting new responsibilities, influencing their teammates and making informed decisions. Empowering employees may improve their confidence, which can help you develop a more active, engaged team.

More creativity

The environment of the coachee during the coaching process favours learning. In addition, the coach encourages the discovery of new alternatives by the coachee, helps connect with the emotional side and unlock the mind to generate new ideas that lead to change. Creativity implies change also because it transforms one reality into another.

It is motivating

Coaching helps to discover the true motivations of the person, what he likes to do. In a systematic way the coachee reaches to understand the true priorities in his life. There is nothing more motivating than fighting for what one really wants.

More growth

Growth and development are one of the rewards coaching offers. This is because the world of coaching focuses on developing the capability of managers and employees at all levels. This helps them perform better in their jobs, qualifying them for higher positions and responsibilities.

Establish and act toward achieving goals

Coaching gives the individual an opportunity to define their career goals in a realistic way. With the assistance of a coach, they can set these goals and then actively work towards them. This will increase the likelihood that the goals will be achieved. It is common for goals to be centered around two aspects of an individual's career. The first is building skill sets, and the second is the individual's professional behavior.

Self-efficacy

The main components of self-efficacy are learning through another's experiences and being affirmed by people you trust. These factors are key building blocks in the coaching relationship. Creating strategies to achieve goals and celebrating those successes with a coach is a prime way to build confidence in oneself.

Build Personal Awareness

A coach can give their coachee ideas for ways to improve themselves, but more importantly they can help them become aware of their blind spots. These blind sports are areas of the individual's work or personality that they may not see, but that need improvement. Once the individual is aware of these areas, they can work with the coach to begin improving them.

Creates a healthier nation

Multi-skills coaching can play a role in ensuring that the health agenda is being met. Different sports need different levels of physical exertion. Using a multi-skill activity for part of your session will ensure heartbeats and breathing rates are elevated, resulting in a fitter and healthier group of participants.

Develops the whole person

Remember that you coach children, not just your sport. Use a multi-skills approach to truly develop multiple skills. Develop social and lifestyle skills as well as physical and sport specific. Multi-skills coaching develops competence, confidence, connection, creativity, character and caring. A multi-skilled athlete should be a multiple-skilled person.

Administration and Organisation

By providing information on program policies and goals, coaches communicate and facilitate the needs of an athlete in an atmosphere of compliance and accountability.

Principles of Officiating

- The principles developing officiating styles.
- Understanding and utilizing sports psychology.
- Communication skills, goal setting and motivation, working effectively with local and regional associations, managing your officiating career.
- The principles of developing a philosophy of officiating.
- The principles developing coaching objectives.
- Principles of Goals and Action Plans.
- Principles of Accountability and Accomplishments.
- Determine your officiating style.
- Set and achieve professional goals.
- Communicate effectively with other officials, coaches, and athletes.

Principles of Coaching

Advocate self-awareness

You want your coachee to learn how to recognize their own strengths and present weaknesses — a prerequisite skill for any good leader. In the same way, you should understand how your own behaviors as a coach impact the people around you. Demonstrate a sense of awareness in yourself and you're more likely to foster in your coachee a similar self-awareness. You may also want to share ways to boost self-awareness.

Promote learning from experience

Most people can learn, grow, and change only if they have the right set of experiences and are open to learning from them. As a coach, always help your coachee reflect on past events and to analyze what went well and what didn't. Foster experiential learning and using experience to fuel development, and your student will continue to improve long after the end of your lessons.

Focus on Coaching the Individual

While the phrase itself can seem misleading, let me clarify it better. As a coach, you need to realize that every client is different and their own person. So, you can't implement a "standard" set of coaching tools on every client who books a coaching session with you. Instead, every client needs individual attention. You need to collect their feedback, understand and listen to their problems and obstacles/challenges, and then partner with them with the right coaching techniques.

Communicate all the time

A big part of coaching is talking often with employees. Meet with them individually on a regular basis, chat with them as they work every day, and be available to answer their questions as much as possible. You'll build trust and learn more about what's going on in your workplace.

Focus on Empowering People

The role of a leadership coach is to bring the clients out of their comfort zone in relation to their goals. Questions and challenges pave the path for change and empowerment. The main objective behind people seeking coaching is because they want to introduce a shift in their lives. Sometimes, the easiest way to help a client find their truth is by asking questions that challenge their boundaries. This is done because leadership coaches trust the true potential and resourcefulness of their clients. So, rooting from the new conscious awareness, the client will adapt themselves to different ways to support their goals by stepping out of their comfort zone and widening their horizons. This form of self-empowerment in a client is relayed through a coach's questioning skills and how they make their clients identify their hidden potential.

Know several ways to coach

As a coach and knowing the key point about coaching others as individual's means that you then need to have several tools in your toolkit of ways to effectively coach and give feedback. It's impossible to coach everyone the way they need to be coached with one dimensional coaching abilities. It's your role to look for, learn and master several coaching skills and feedback techniques.

Set Intentions
Setting clear intentions at the start of your journey with a new client not only creates clear expectations, but also helps you track progress over the long-term. You and your client will be able to see the magic and the results of your work together.

Observe
Coaches need to be adept at getting information from employees without making people feel as if they're being interrogated or spied on. Talk to your people and observe them at work to identify skill deficiencies and any other areas of their job they might be confused about.

Outlook of Officials and Coaches towards Management, Players and Spectators

Coaches teach amateur or professional athletes the skills they need to succeed at their sport. Sports Coaches, Instructors and Officials coach, train and instruct participants in sports, and officiate at sporting events.

- Planning and directing game strategies, developing play patterns and analysing game progress.
- Motivating Sportspersons and supervising practice sessions.
- Recruiting players and other coaching staff.
- Arranging entries into sporting competitions.
- Promoting sports and skills development, and overseeing the participation of young people in sport.
- Officiating at sporting events to enforce rules.
- Participating in recruiting and scouting activities
- Monitoring the performance of individual athletes.
- Teaching and mentoring the athletes on all aspects of their sport.
- Monitoring the athletic eligibility of student athletes.
- Encouraging good sportsmanship and fostering strong character among athletes.
- Supervising athletes in practice areas, on buses and inside locker rooms.
- Maintaining the individual's or team's uniforms and equipment.

Measures for Improving the Standards of Officiating and Coaching

Controlling game is most important. How an official can control the game depends on his or her philosophy and mental quality pertaining to appearance, communication, method of handling conflicts and how they behave in tough situations. Officials should have the wisdom and rules knowledge to make decisions that keep the good of their sport in the forefront. Officials should be paying attention to the non-verbal messages being relayed by players and coaches before they boil over and become verbally abusive or even physical in nature. Listen with your ears and your eyes. No one should underestimate the value of appearance. Buy the standard clothes and equipment for your level of play and wear them properly. Iron your shirts and pants, and shine your shoes.

Be dressed and ready before you appear on the field or court and dress professionally when arriving at your changing room before the game. Looks are seldom deceiving; make sure your first impression is one that you can try to live up to and not one that you have to overcome. Presenting yourself as a professional includes your physical appearance and knowledge of the game. Arriving to the event early in a clean uniform is the first step in making a good impression and gaining respect. Knowing the rules is paramount. Officials can be excused for missing a call, but not for misinterpreting or misstating the rules. Coaches, players and spectators know when an official is prepared and working hard on the playing field. The rulebook attorneys are hypercritical. They memorize the rules, can quote casebook plays precisely without hesitation and are predominantly reactionary officials. When they see something happen, they react quickly, they apply the rule under all situations and move on to the next play. They are analytical in their officiating approach, almost engineering-like, never a variation.

Coaching is a powerful role and most people want to make a good impression on you. So if you show any emotion, your coachee will react and adapt what they are saying, which negatively impacts their thinking space. Feedback can take many different forms, but without it, athletes don't know what to keep doing, and how to improve. Remember that feedback is not always expressed in words. It is easy for athletes to pick up on frowns and hostile body language. Young athletes don't instinctively know what they need to do to perform at their peak-level, and this is where consistent feedback comes in. This feedback should be both positive and constructive. After a loss, it can be difficult to point out the positives, but that's your job, as a coach.

UNIT-II

Coaching

Philosophy of Coaching

A coaching philosophy is a statement or few statements about what you value and how you approach your role as a coach. It also addresses your purpose, beliefs, and principles. A coaching philosophy is a coaching tool to help guide coaches in their process of coaching. Having a philosophy gives a coach clear guidance on the objectives that should be pursued and how to achieve them. A coach's stand is a great way for a coach to begin effectively determining their coaching philosophy. Your coaching philosophy goes beyond the techniques and tactics of your sport. It's a set of values, beliefs and guiding principles that determine how you coach. You need to think bigger than the 'game' and allow it to be shaped by your experiences as a person.

Your coaching philosophy guides how you behave as a coach and how you interact with your athletes. It should reflect who you are and who you want to be. It is based on your experiences, knowledge, values, opinions and beliefs. Of these, your values have the greatest impact on your coaching philosophy, as it is a statement of what is important to you. If your philosophy is clearly defined, you can set any ethical issues or dilemmas clearly within that structure. This will make it easier to avoid problems and make sure that you behave consistently. Everyone that coaches has a coaching philosophy; not everyone has taken the time to examine it and write it down. If you have not examined it, then your coaching philosophy will be at a subconscious level. It will still be impacting on how you coach, however, without a clear understanding of what it is you are unable to ensure that it is appropriate. As a young coach, you will create a dynamic philosophy that will continue to evolve throughout your career until such time as you are comfortable and confident with the way you make decisions for your team.

Your coaching philosophy inevitably is shaped by the experiences you gain working with different athletes in various situations. Ultimately, your philosophy comprises the values you hold in highest regard and the ones you are comfortable sharing with and teaching to the athletes that make up your team. A coach should also lead with their words and their actions. As a coach, we communicate with our athletes verbally and with our actions. A coach should not only verbally promote key values such as trust, commitment, teamwork, and respect but a coach should be setting an example with how they interact with their athletes, fellow coaches, and colleagues. Preaching these values only goes so far; athletes need to see that the values being told to them are important to the coaches as well.

Great coaches are able to get more out of their athletes, develop mind-sets year after year for decades, and build cultures of winning. They are successful because they have a consistent set of values and goals which guide their actions. They are successful because they are driven by something greater than wins and losses. Your coaching philosophy can differentiate you from other coaches and help clients trust you, especially if they have similar values and beliefs. Philosophy is integrated in almost everything. We all have philosophies in which our reasons and what we do with our days are centred. Everyone has a philosophy of life that is their own; every organisation has a philosophy.

Coach as a Mentor

A mentor is someone who shares their knowledge, skills and/or experience, to help another to develop and grow. A coach is someone who provides guidance to a client on their goals and helps them reach their full potential.

Duties of a Coach in General

A good coach should do a full health and safety check of the surroundings and participants before any activity starts. This can include checking for jewellery, appropriate clothing. Coaches promote physical, psychological and social benefits for athletes and encourage sport participation. Coaches plan, teach, assess and adapt in order to conduct quality sport practices and prepare for competition. Sports coaches train individual athletes and teams to help them improve their overall physical condition and address specific fitness or physical issues. A coach may offer specific advice to an individual team member who's returning to practice after an injury or illness. Coaches often simulate real-world or competition conditions in their training sessions.

Pre-game

- Arrive at clubhouse 3 hours prior to game time
- Lay out supplies for taping
- Prepare Medical Supply Kits to be taken to the game
- Ensure crutches, ice and ice bags, and water bottles are packed
- Ensure you arrive at the field at least 1 hour prior to game time
- Set up supplies at field
- Do any last minute taping, spatting etc.

During game

- Communicate to position coach and head coach injured athlete status if necessary.
- Clarify Field and Bench Assignments.
- Field Staff: watch the field for mechanism of injury and enter the field when called upon to attend to an injured player.
- Bench Staff is responsible for any taping, bandaging, other treatment and facilitation of assessments by training staff and or the team doctors.

Post-game

- Provide summary of injuries to coaching staff.
- Pack up supplies, ensure nothing remains behind on the benches or dressing room.
- Make list of any players requiring further post-game assessments.
- Provide any necessary treatment or follow up.

Responsibilities of a Coach on and Off the Field

As coach your skills require you to focusing on the goal, actively listen to what is being said by the coachee, use a variety of question types to tease the ideas from the coachee, and be non-judgmental in the feedback you give. These skills require you to make a conscious effort to control you initial instincts when a problem arises. You have to resist wanting to direct, resolve and judge the situation. Instead as coach you need to be the catalyst for change in a non-judgmental way by taking on the role of facilitator, listener and questioner. Coaches are required to warn parents and athletes of unsafe practices specific to a sport and the potential for injury or death. This warning should be issued in writing and both athletes and parents should be required to provide written certification of their comprehension. Coaches should demonstrate model behaviour at all times. Their influence should always be positive and would usually mean working to a code. They must act in the most ethical and professional manner, showing a degree of honest, integrity and competence. They should be considerate of all individual needs and do their best to accommodate for everyone. Coaching will spend a lot of time working with children and young performers so are likely to develop a closer relationship, becoming maybe a parent figure or friend. Therefore they need to be aware of what is considered inappropriate contact or behaviour that may breach child protection guidelines.

Coaches should have sport specific skills as they need to understand certain technical aspects of the sport they are trying to teach. A coach needs to ensure that they have a good knowledge and understanding of their own sport and how the latest information in sport science can aid to develop performers, this is important so coaches can deliver demonstrations correctly and carry out good practice as if they were to demonstrate something wrongly then students could pick up bad habits by simply imitating and doing as their instructed. However if a coach is less knowledgeable in a particular area of sport they could use their transferable skills.

Coaching ultimately leads to better overall results for the company or business. When done well coaching can increase productivity, bring a greater sense of commitment and loyalty from team members as they feel more connected and valued, this will also work towards reducing stress and tension as staff feel supported and heard and will improve overall communication. A coach must be physically present, provide competent instruction, structure practices that are appropriate for the age and maturity of players, prevent foreseeable injuries and respond to injury or trauma in an approved manner. This duty requires supervisors to make sure facilities are locked and that students are denied access when a competent staff member cannot be physically present to supervise. This duty may also require coaches to control reckless player behaviors. Supervision responsibility also pertains to athletic administrators who are expected to be able to supervise coaches competently. The purpose of coaching within the workplace is to improve working performance. Like a stereotypical sports coach, a workplace coach takes the existing skills of a team or individual and builds on them, enhances them and gets the very best from them. They will also introduce new skills and give them the knowledge and ability to use them.

Psychological Aspects during Competition and Coaching

Psychological coaching is a process that aims to help clients achieve concrete goals, identify and overcome obstacles to well-being and performance, and build skills that may be interfering with their success. Coaching comes from the world of sports, where athletes have coaches who help them improve their performance. It has then evolved into increasing performance in general, such as in the workplace. In short, the psychology of competition indicates it's beneficial to compete in small rather than large groups. This has implications, for example, in the workplace and in the classroom, or any other setting where competition is a significant factor. Individual factors are those that differ from one person to the next, such as the importance of the performance dimension, the similarity of rivals and their proximity to the individual, and the other individual differences variables linked to social comparison in general.

Coaching is specific, goal-oriented, and can be conducted one-on-one or in a group. Like sports coaching, psychological coaching concentrates on individual or group strengths and abilities and how they might be used in new and different ways to enhance performance, feel better about the self, ensure smooth life transitions, strengthen relationships, deal with challenges, achieve goals, become more successful, or improve the overall quality of one's personal and professional life. Competition gives incentives for self-improvement. If two watchmakers are competing for business, they will lower their prices and improve their products to increase their sales. During a game or contest, a competitive person may go to great lengths to be victorious. Competitiveness can motivate a person to work harder than they would have alone. However, an individual who feels they must win at all costs may burn themselves out or alienate others. When competitiveness causes emotional distress or disrupts someone's daily life, that person may wish to get professional help. The practice of coaching psychology may be described as a process for enhancing well-being and performance in personal life and work domains underpinned by models of coaching grounded in established adult and child learning or psychological theories and approaches. It is practised by qualified coaching psychologists who have relevant qualifications, and have undertaken suitable continuing professional development and supervised practice.

UNIT-III

Duties of Official

Philosophy of Officiating

Officials should have the wisdom and rules knowledge to make decisions that keep the good of their sport in the forefront. Some officials operate in this stringent way. They believe that by applying rules in a punitive manner, they are fulfilling their role as the game's guardian. But the rules of any sport are subject to wide interpretation simply because there are so many variations in game circumstances. Officiating philosophy is described as who we are and how we handle game situations. Remember, we have the responsibility to be the guardians of the game. This is an awesome, yet important responsibility that we need to take seriously. The game belongs to the kids playing it. Remember no matter what the age of the players, it's their game, not ours. Developing an officiating philosophy is an important skill for success. Officiating is like a three-legged stool. One leg being rule knowledge, another leg is mechanics, and the third leg is philosophy. If one leg is weak, the stool will topple. When all three legs of the officiating stool are strong we have a game that players can play, the coaches can coach, and the fans can enjoy. Controlling the game is most important. How an official can control the game depends on his or her philosophy and mental quality pertaining to appearance, communication, method of handling conflicts and how they behave in tough situations. For most it can take years to develop and certainly your philosophy changes over time as you mature.

Duties of Official in General

Officials are responsible for ensuring that the sport is played safely. This may involve intervening in altercations between opposing players and administering penalties or ejections if warranted, and possibly reporting flagrant behavior to league officials. They also check players' uniforms and equipment to verify compliance with safety rules. Officials must have a thorough knowledge of the rules of the sport and be able to enforce them during play. This can involve studying the sport's rule book, as well as attending classes or seminars. Some sports organizations review and update their rules annually, so continuous study is often necessary. While officials typically do not keep the time in sports that use a clock, they keep an eye on the clock to ensure it is started and stopped properly. If discrepancies arise, officials direct the timekeeper to make the necessary corrections. Sports officials are responsible for maintaining integrity and fairness. They need a deep love of the sport they're officiating and belief in the concept of fair play. Without umpires and referees sport wouldn't function at all, so they're very important roles. Sports officiating is very flexible and usually pays reasonably well. It's particularly good for people who want to supplement their income with a small part-time role or for those working around their studies. The further up the ladder you go, the better the quality of sport on offer too, so you might end up working with some very talented sportspeople.

Pre-game

Arrive early

When officials arrive at the rink early, they often will walk around the arena or grab something to drink from the concession stand. This time provides the official an excellent opportunity to inspect certain aspects such as, where the scoreboard is located, the access to the rink for players and officials, and other rink characteristics that may come into play during the game.

- At least 15 minutes prior to game time (20-30 minutes if first game of the day).
- In proper uniform: jersey, shorts, black socks, and badge.
- With required equipment: Watch, pens, whistle, coin, flags, and data wallet.

Check field and equipment

- Nets (secured, no holes/gaps).
- Corner flags.
- Markings.
- Holes, glass, rocks, debris, etc.
- Goals (properly secured).

Check players equipment

- Shin guards must be under the socks (completely covered–safety issue).

- Team Uniform: Shirt, Shorts, Shoes, Socks, Shin guards.
- If thermal shorts are worn, they must be the same color as the shorts.
- Goalkeeper's shirt must be distinguishable.
- Home team players/coaches should be checked first but it's not a requirement. You should start with the team that appears to be most ready for inspection.
- Make sure that all jewellery, earrings, watches, etc. have been removed. A medical ID must be taped to the player's chest or taped to the wrist with the info showing. (Earrings must be removed. Covering them with tape does not make them legal).
- All players must wear shin guards and socks must be pulled over shin guards.
- Player's shirts are to be tucked in.
- Check in players and coaches as per the requirements and the Rules of Competition for that league.

During game

- Ensure player safety and maintain the integrity of the game.
- Enforce game rules and Intramural policies.
- Promote sportsmanship among players.
- Receive feedback from Intramural Supervisors and apply instruction.

Post-game

- Assist with field and playing equipment storage and administrative functions.
- Provide positive public relations, program promotion, and policy education to participants.
- Provide a friendly, upbeat and customer service oriented environment at all times.

Technical and Tactical Preparation of an Official

The aim of technical preparation is to create and improve sports skills. Each sports skill has a given way of solving a motor task (contents of a sports skill) in accordance with the rules of a given sport, biomechanical rules and locomotive possibilities of the athlete which are referred to as technique. Specific individual adjustment of technique by an athlete is referred to as style. Technical skills are how athletes in different sports move their bodies to achieve certain targets. Successful athletes master a wide range of technical skills that allow them to be successful in their chosen sport. Every sport has its own set of technical skills, and in some sports, skills with identical or similar names are actually different techniques. Tactical skills are strategic mental abilities that successful athletes use to win games and competitions. Mastering these skills can help an athlete or team use their techniques effectively. They might involve problem-solving skills and often rely on the athlete's knowledge of their coach's goals. Many of these skills can apply to multiple sports.

Ethics of Officiating

Officials shall display and execute superior communication skills, both verbal and non-verbal. Officials shall remain mindful that their conduct influences the respect that student- athletes, coaches and the public hold for the profession. Officials shall, while enforcing the rules of play, remain aware of the inherent risk of injury that competition poses to student-athletes. Where appropriate, they shall inform event management of conditions or situations that appear unreasonably hazardous. Officials shall take reasonable steps to educate themselves in the recognition of emergency conditions that might arise during the course of competition. Officials shall maintain an ethical approach while participating in forums, chat rooms and all forms of social media.

According to National Association of Sports Officials, Officials shall bear a great responsibility for engendering public confidence in sports. Officials shall be free of obligation to any interest other than the impartial and fair judging of sports competitions. Officials shall hold and maintain the basic tenets of officiating which include history, integrity, neutrality, respect, sensitivity, professionalism, discretion and tactfulness. Officials shall master both rules of the game and mechanics necessary to enforce the rules, and shall exercise authority in an impartial, firm and controlled manner.

UNIT-IV

Qualities and qualification of Coach and Official

Qualities and Qualification of an Efficient Coach

Discipline

An effective coach clearly states a code of conduct up front and adheres to it. Evidence supports that for discipline to effectively change behaviour, it must be mild, prompt and consistent. Athletes need to adhere to a reasonable set of rules both on and off the field and if these are ignored you are responsible for discipline. Trust between athlete and coach is of paramount importance at all times and essential for successful coaching.

A good coach is self-aware

Self-awareness is a journey unto itself, so we'll be writing more about that in the coming weeks. To understand oneself, one's coaching style, and how it is perceived and received by employees, is a critical first step to becoming a valuable and effective coach.

Commitment

Being a coach is not easy but it can be incredibly rewarding. But to reap those rewards, a great coach has to be committed. This refers not only to the sport at hand but also committed to showing up for their team members consistently. It also means taking the time to commit and communicate effectively with team member's parents and educate them when necessary. The important thing to remember is that every coach will be more successful if they can get the parents to work with them and not against them.

Honesty

Honesty sometimes hurts, but it is critical to improvement and setting realistic goals. This is a tricky one, but one that I find is absolutely vital to success. It's also one of the harder issues to address between coach and athlete. When looking for a coach, spend some time asking this coach how they can tell you how realistic your goals are and what you need to do to improve your swimming, cycling or running. You are really doing yourself a disservice if you do not hire someone who has experience in handling tough conversations about what is realistic for you in regards to progress, race results and realistic time goals.

Perceptiveness

Each athlete is so different. A good coach recognizes that and writes challenging workouts for each individual person. A good coach should be able to figure you out. A coach should be able to read each athlete, determine what their strengths are, which workouts would help them improve and which ones would not, and create programs that are individualized to bring the best out of you.

Provides Personal Guidance

Excellent coaching requires the ability to treat athletes as more than sports figures. You must have a genuine concern for the players' personal lives, rather than viewing outside influences as distractions. These occurrences present additional opportunities to reinforce learning. During these challenges, your actions may not align with moving the team toward victory, but you must place the players' well-being before the game.

Observant

Great coaches are highly observant and have an incredible ability to read between the lines. They're able to pick up and interpret the tiniest change in a client. A shift in the tone of voice, a raised eyebrow, a clearing of the throat and long pauses between sentences. One of the best coaching qualities is understanding how to read body language. Great coaches notice body language cues and can interpret what they see, hear and feel from a client, accurately.

Goal-Focused

The coach should be able to set up the day to day plan for you, but also be able to see the big picture, set up a macro plan and be able to explain to you why the workouts and races are structured like they are to achieve your goals. Make sure your coach asks you what your goals are and what you want to accomplish, both short- and long-term.

Good Listener

The effective coach will seek out information from the players. Finally, the good coach will be flexible and will use player feedback to modify the training plan if necessary. Part of communicating effectively is listening. A coach should be a compassionate ear and should welcome the players' comments, questions, and input.

Understanding the sport

Coaches must plan for the season, know the progressive nature of training adaptation, know the rules, and provide a simple, structured environment for athletes to succeed. To be able to teach effectively, you must have in-depth understanding of the sport from the fundamental skills to advanced tactics and strategy.

Sharing knowledge

Obtaining knowledge is important but having the confidence to share and seek others' views, especially those outside of your sport, is a key quality. The best coaches clearly understand they are there to educate the athletes. Most athletes spend most of the time training on their own, so the more they really understand what they are doing and why they are doing it the better they will train and practise.

Expertise

Coaches are to be well-conversant with their domain and assigned tasks. Certainly, a good coach needs to possess thorough knowledge in his or her field. He should be at home as regards the rudimentary skills to advanced techniques and overall game plan. A coach might have experience as a player in his or her career; however, to be a successful coach needs specific expertise and in-depth knowledge of the game. The coach must have a distinct skill to devise a season plan, understand the growing and ongoing methods of training, keep abreast of the rules, and create a well-organized environment for players to get through.

Goal-oriented

Great mentors know short-term goals are just as important as long-term ones. If you know what your long-term goals are, a mentor can help you develop a goal-setting strategy that will achieve lasting results. This will make your objective feel more attainable, and you'll feel a sense of accomplishment checking smaller items off your to-do list as you work toward your larger goal.

Flexibility

Good coaches are flexible. They are not only looking for ways to improve themselves but also how they approach and communicate with each individual team member. They understand that not everyone learns the same way and are willing to change their approach in order to help their team member master a particular technique. Coaches who are flexible are more effective than coaches who aren't willing to adapt to the student and insist on teaching or coaching every student the same way.

Quality Feedback

Ask the coach how they will provide feedback to you on your workouts and races. Progress is the name of the game and if the athlete does not feel they're making progress, they should be able to ask the coach for feedback on how to change things up. Also, the coach should be able to provide feedback on your workouts and data, tell you how to move things around when you're sick or traveling, and adapt schedules on the fly. They should also be able to give you specific training feedback such as how to improve your swim stroke, for example.

Motivator

A coach should make sure that players understand that you can completely control your own effort and training, but can't control what your opponent does or the outcome of every match. The successful coach is a motivator with a positive attitude and enthusiasm for the game and the players. The ability to motivate and inspire is part of the formula for success. Getting athletes to believe in themselves and achieve come far easier from some coaches than others. The coach who can motivate is able to generate the desire to excel in their athletes. Motivation may mean keeping the practice fun, fresh and challenging. When motivating a player, a good coach stresses trying to reach performance goals, not outcome goals.

Communication and Listening Skills

A great coach should also be able to listen to your team members, not only to receive input from them but also to be willing to listen and understand when a team member is going through a difficult situation in their life or when they need to adjust their training schedule for whatever reason. Aside from knowing all the intricacies of the sport, a good coach needs to have excellent communication and listening skills. After all, all the knowledge in the world is useless unless your coach can communicate the message effectively to your team members. When your coach can easily explain the why behind each training session or the reason for a particular strategy, your team members will be better prepared and know what to do in certain situations.

Inspires Self-Realization

A good coach knows how to motivate athletes without using negative reinforcement, which can achieve short-term results but eventually does more harm than good. As a coach, your job is to help the team members believe in themselves and consistently perform beyond their own expectations. To help them reach their full potential, you must motivate the players to think outside of their mental comfort zones.

Teaches Transferable Skills

To coach effectively, your lessons should apply to life as well as the game. This means teaching more than game-related skills. Every challenge presents opportunities to provide life lessons. This requires careful consideration of the messages that you relay. By providing relevant and non-judgmental critiques, you can build the players' self-esteem while providing valuable guidance. You can accomplish this by paying close attention to their statements and actions, verbally clarifying the responses and providing affirmative feedback.

Supportive

Great coaches take their clients struggles seriously, no matter how small or insignificant these may seem. Great coaches have an incredible ability to walk a mile in their client's shoes yet retain enough distance to see the big picture and offer guidance and direction.

Understanding

While many might not initially jump to rank humility and a sense of compassionate understanding very highly in coaching necessities, they truly are valuable commodities to possess here. The compassionate and humble coach understands what players and adversaries feel and think. This additional insight makes the coach even more valuable in all means of strategy and forecast. Acting on that very insight in a caring and respectable way makes them even greater as a coach and as a human.

Strategic
One of the most important qualities of a good coach and mentor is that they will make sure you are properly prepared in order to meet your goals. This means practicing the little things you need to succeed day in and day out.

Qualification of coach

A coach must help students realise their inherent knowledge and abilities to attain a long-term goal. As a coach, it's your job to make sure the trainee can apply what they've learned in the classroom to real-world scenarios. A degree in sports management may be obtained from various educational institutions. Applicants for these diploma programmes must have completed a 10+2 or an equivalent. Some institutions may also need their students to be college graduates to be qualified for the degrees in sports coaching given by them. In the hands of a coach, it is possible to turn raw potential into champions. To solve a current issue or attain a particular goal in an event, a coach helps the participant narrow their focus.

Qualities and Qualification of an Efficient Official

A Calm Attitude
Officials must learn how to stay calm and listen to the players and coaches at all times but must maintain at least a language barrier for better communication. All sports need good communication with the officials to have a nice and fair game. New officials must know when to stay silent and when to stay away from confrontations. They also need to learn how to handle a situation calmly. They have to develop these characteristics to become a better officials. Officials need to stay calm at all times to control the game properly. Remaining calm during the game influences other athletes and officials as well. Officials that keep their cool during the game can also have a good relationship with the coaches, which will help in resolving tense situations. Officials also gain respect from all the people involved in the sport if they know they can handle any situation with composure.

Integrity

An official holds a position in the world of sports not unlike a judge in a court of law. If you aspire to be a great official, you must never put yourself in a position where your integrity could be questioned. A great sports official is the last guardian of honesty in athletics. He must maintain a complete absence of bias. We can read almost daily of coaches, players and boosters engaging in illegal activities. Referees and umpires are rarely accused of any kind of dishonest or deceitful conduct. Simple advice: If there is any possibility of a conflict of interest, don't work the game.

Consistency

Inconsistent decisions on similar plays trigger negative behavior and poor sportsmanship among players, and invite criticism from coaches. Young officials have more difficulty with consistency than any other quality, mainly because they lack the experience to realize when their decisions are inconsistent. Everyone has some difficulty in this regard, but the great officials are unrelenting in their judgment. They see and call a game better than their colleagues. The key is to make the same call on the same kind of play whether it's the first minute of the game or the score is tied with one minute left to play. If they believe an official is consistent, coaches and players will adjust accordingly.

Approachability

Along with having a calming presence, being approachable was another quality listed for officials who get noticed in a positive way. From the situation with the coach in the example above, Rolf was accessible and approachable, something that gave the coach a comfort zone with her.

Game Management

If you handle a big situation correctly, coaches and officials will respect you. Cress called the ability to handle situations another important factor that sets apart the special official the one everyone wants. In softball, that means being ready for the second or third play in a sequence, not just the routine ground ball. If, for example, all you are ready for is the basic grounder, then the throw goes wide at first, you may just react to the second incident instead of being ahead of the play.

Hustle

Being quick and running a lot does not necessarily make you a good official. Every great referee moves efficiently to be in the right place at the right time in order to see the spaces between the players. It's the only way to see the whole play, from the best angle, to see the spaces means that you can also make good decisions on the responsibility for contact and then have a good chance to make the correct decision. Hustle also means that your movement in dead ball situations such as moving to the table to a new position, should not be done whilst walking. Move efficiently and with a purpose and keep the game moving with your hustle. Officiating is game of angles, positioning and movement. This is true for the players and should also therefore be the same for the referees. Hustle describes this movement to a position on the court. There is no connection to speed and meaningless motion.

Confidence

Officials must have confidence in themselves in how they will officiate a game. They must be comfortable with their knowledge and skills in handling the entire duration of the game. Part of good officiating is their confidence in making decisions in making solutions for difficult situations. Confidence takes a lot of work and experience with the fundamentals of the sport.

Good Judgment

The good judgment applies through the critical principles of the advantages and disadvantages of the rules of the sport. It simply means no harm, no foul. Great judgment can be a result of effort and experience. Few officials are born with it and many have to work hard at it. Therefore, it can also be described as an instinctive ability to apply the principals of advantage/disadvantage. When you see a play, in almost every case, if there is no advantage gained and if no player has been put at a disadvantage, there should be no call. One of the most important characteristics of an Officials is having good judgment during the game, especially in the most intense situations where players and coaches depend on the Officials call. It is a by-product of experience and hard work through the knowledge of the sport itself.

Courage

Regardless of the situation, personalities involved, pressures from the crowd or possible repercussions, great officials place fairness above all other concerns. They act courageously and according to the dictates of that value. The world of sports is full of people with high morale and enthusiasm in winning the game and beating their opponents. Officials should expect different personalities, pressure from spectators, repercussions, and seasoned officials that they will have to deal with during a game. An Officials should stay courageous at all times and should not let anybody dictate their judgments in officiating the game.

Common sense

Common sense ensures that fairness, understanding, and the best interests of the game are foremost in the mind of the referee. If you truly understand the spirit and the intent of the rules, common sense will guide you well. Plenty of game situations develop that are not specifically covered by rules or mechanics. That's when common sense must take over. What is fair or what is right, is what should be done. Common sense goes hand in hand with Communication and dealing with coaches and players. It helps determine how to handle a tough situation and for example, whether a technical foul should or should not be called. Of all the qualities an Officials must possess, common sense is the most important. That which is fair and right should always take precedence in every contest.

Motivated

Like the players and coaches, an Officials should also be motivated in doing their task in officiating a game. They must have a positive mental attitude and feel lively during the game to help them make the right calls. An Officials must also be dedicated and hard-working to increase their levels of motivation, which will also help them enjoy every moment of their task in a game. Feeling less motivated affects their officiating and will lead to complicated situations because of misunderstandings.

Physical fitness

It is really impossible for an Officials to make mistakes at the end of the contest, which may affect the outcome of the game. Your fitness will have at some stage, a direct effect on how you perform in a game whether the effect is good or bad, will depend on the investment an official has made in his fitness. It has long been recognized and proven, that there is a direct connection between your physical condition and your mental state. If you become physically tired during, or especially towards the end of a game, then your level of concentration will also suffer, or decline. The modern professional players are in great shape and so the referee must also be in good shape, to keep pace with the game for all four quarters. Games can be decided in the last quarter or of course even in the final seconds.

Qualification of Official

Former and senior player of the sports can start their career in the field as an assistant referee to gain some on filed experience before handling the job independently. However, those aspirants who have a non-playing background but know and understand the game well can take some formal training to enter this profession. Although 10+2 is the basic requirement for any aspiring candidate to enter the profession the Umpiring or referring but to participate in the national and international level games as a referee one should be at least a graduate. Educational requirements vary by state and are sometimes determined by the local sports association. Although some states have no formal education requirements, other states require umpires, referees, and other sports officials to have a high school diploma. Training requirements also vary by state and the level and type of sport. All sports, however, require extensive knowledge of the rules of the game.

Current Status of Coaching and Officiating in India

The coaching programme aims to train up the players in a way that they can represent the State in International and National level competitions and bring laurels to the state. The coaching is provided in the Sarusajai Sports Complex, Sarusajai, Guwahati and LNIPE, Tepesia to give exposure and experience to the budding sports talents of the state to train in state of the art sports facilities. The Coaching is imparted by the Coaches and Trainers of International and National repute. The State Level Coaches will assist the chief coaches in imparting training to the front ranking players. Umpires, referees, carry out official duties at tournaments and matches and enforce penalties as per the rules and regulations of the different games. Umpires, referees, position themselves to see the action, judge the situation, and conclude any violations. Some sports officials, such as badminton officials, work alone, while swimming officials work in group.

Measures for Improving the Standard of Coaching and Officiating in India

- Create a safe environment.
- Set up an informal routine.
- Align interests to goals & objectives.
- Listen and observe.
- Ask the HOW and WHAT questions.
- Appreciate good work.
- Prepare for constructive feedback.
- Be open to feedback yourself.

Role of Impartial Officiating and Coaching In Maintaining Integrity and Values of Sports

Sports officials must be able to bring control to chaos, understand fairness, promote safety and encourage good sportsmanship. A sports official must have the positive characteristics of a police officer, lawyer, judge, accountant, reporter, athlete and diplomat. They are also someone who can be put in a position of authority and handle the responsibility without being overbearing. The word integrity means to be whole and undivided but also the quality of being honest with strong moral principles. In sport, this means the manifestation of the ethics and values which promote confidence in sports, including positive conduct by its members and community. Hence, the purpose of the sport integrity framework is to protect against illegal and immoral activities. Integrity is the most fundamental value of sport. Integrity in sport is largely addressed through concepts of fair play, respect for the game, sportsmanship, positive personal values of responsibility, compassion for the other, and honesty in adhering to rules. Corruption erodes the very spirit of sport. Without integrity, competitive sports are meaningless. Breaches of integrity not only damage values like fair play, honour and dignity of athletes and nations, but also shape a sport's popularity, its business, sponsorship viability and even its survival. Many sports have taken active steps towards safeguarding competitions.

Sport can teach values such as fairness, teambuilding, equality, discipline, inclusion, perseverance and respect. Sport has the power to provide a universal framework for learning values, thus contributing to the development of soft skills needed for responsible citizenship. Sports are essential parts of our lives because they assist our bodies in growing physically and mentally. Sports are considered the best exercise since they keep our bodies healthy and energized. A successful person must be both intellectually and physically fit. A physically active person is psychologically healthy and well, and having a healthy mind is always advantageous. On the other hand, an unhealthy person leads a terrible and pathetic lifestyle, and his life sometimes becomes a burden for himself.

Technical Officials levels

A Technical Official is defined as any person who controls the play of a competition by applying the rules and regulations of the sport to make judgments on rule infringement, performance, time or ranking.

Level I
The objective of the Level I Course is to provide participants with the theoretical and practical training required to make them capable of officiating at national level competitions and at international competitions held within the country.

Level II
The objective of the Level II Course is to provide participants with the theoretical and practical training required to make them capable of officiating at international competitions up to the Area level.

Level III
The objective of the Level III Course is to provide participants with the theoretical and practical training required to make them capable of officiating at international competitions up to the highest level.

Exams of Various Games (An Introduction)

Games and Sports is a very common and useful topics of the Government competitive exams. At first you need to gather basic terms and awards of the specific games. Not only Cricket and Football all the other games that means Hockey, Lawn Tennis, Table Tennis, Badminton Etc. are also very important for the competitive exams. Country-wise National Games, Some basic concept about the specific game is the key area, from that segment randomly questions have been asked in the very recent competitive examinations. Any sports or game is designated as the national game of the country either on the basis of its popularity or based on its historical connection with that country. Sports terms form an important part of the general awareness section of competitive exams. It is one of the most common questions asked in various government exams.

Practical Course

Course Code: PED301PR

Specialization in Volleyball

UNIT-I

History of Game

Volleyball is a widely popular team sport played on a rectangular court divided evenly by a standing net. The object of volleyball is to score more points than the opposing team. This is done by sending the ball over the net and grounding it inside the opposing team's court before its players are able to hit it back over the net and ground it inside their opposition's court. However, whether one wins or loses, each player's strenuous and constant activities during the play of volleyball results in a physically fit body and good cardiovascular health.

William Morgan invented the game of Volleyball in 1885. He was an athletic director at the YMCA and was trying to emulate basketball and came up with volleyball. Since then, the rules have changed here and there, but it quickly became a popular sport at the YMCA. The name volleyball came about when a man named Alfred Halstead noticed how the game had a volleying nature. People declared it the name of volleyball and the name got stuck. The game of volleyball was first played in the Olympics in the

1964 edition. Japan won the first gold medal in the women's category of volleyball whereas USSR won the first gold in the men's category of volleyball.

Measurement and Preparation of the Play Field

The volleyball court is 18 meters long and 9 meters wide. It's divided into sides in the middle by the net. The width of the net is 1 m and is set up at the height of 7 feet 11 5/8 inches above the ground (8 feet approx).

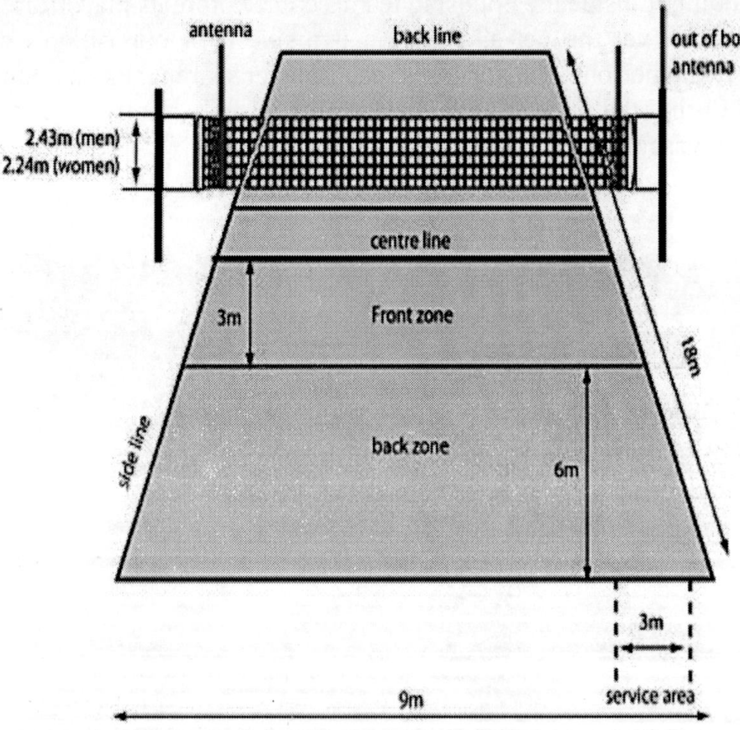

The other key feature is a line that is drawn on each side 3 m from the net & parallel to the net. This line is called the attack line. It defines the front row and back row sections of the Volleyball court.

Equipment Required For Game

Ball

Volley ball a spherical ball of 65-67 cm circumference. It is made of leather or any synthetic material and weighs 260-280 g. Volleyballs are available in various colours, however for international tournaments, FIVB approved balls should only be used.

Net and Court

The outdoor volleyball court measures 18 x 9 m, surrounded by a free zone that is 2 meters wide on all sides. The minimum playing space for U.S. volleyball competitions is 7 meters. The volleyball net is 32 feet long by 3 feet wide. For women's volleyball, the net height should be 7 feet, 4 1/8 inches high. For men's volleyball, the net height should be 7 feet, 11 5/8 inches high. U.S. regulation volleyball playing surfaces must be flat and not present any hazards to the players in the middle or on the sides of the court.

Fundamental Skills and Lead-Up Games

Serving

The serve is the first contact in a volleyball game, and it's an important opportunity to gain an advantage over the opposing team. It is a skill that every player must master as it's the first move that can give your team momentum and shut down your opponent's momentum.

Passing

Also known as the bump, is used to receive the ball from the opposing team's serve or hit. The goal of passing is to keep the ball in play and set up an offensive play. To pass effectively, the player should get in position, keep their arms straight and feet parallel, extend their knees forward, and make contact with the ball using their forearms.

Setting

Setting in volleyball is the second hit after a bump or dig that sets up a teammate for a spike. Setting is crucial in volleyball, as a good set can enable your opponent to win the point with a well-placed spike, while a bad set will put your team out of position and possibly cost you the point.

Hitting

Once the first and second players on a volleyball team have contacted the ball by passing or setting, it is up to the rest of the players to set up an attack in order to send the ball back over the net. The most common way to do this is by hitting, which is a sharp, usually overhand blow to the ball designed to send it over the net.

Block

The first line of defense. Used to try to stop the ball from entering your court, but should also funnel the attack to a smaller area of the court making it easier for your defenders.

Digging

Digging is a defensive skill used to save the ball from hitting the ground. It is often done when the ball does not come directly at the player, and a standard underhand pass would be impossible or extremely difficult to get. To get into a digging position, the player must sink their hips low to the floor with their heels slightly raised in order to be light on their feet. They must then stretch out their arms into the underhand pass position.

Techniques, Strategies and Method of Play

- Toss the ball in front of your serving shoulder.
- Keep your elbow high and back.
- Contact the middle of the ball with the middle of your hand.
- Follow through on your arm swing.

Rules and Regulations of the Game

- Only 6 players on the floor at any given time: 3 in the front row and 3 in the back row.
- Points are made on every serve for the winning team of the rally (rally-point scoring).
- Players may not hit the ball twice in succession (a block is not considered a hit).
- Ball may be played off the net during a volley and on a serve.
- A ball hitting a boundary line is in.
- A ball is out if it hits an antennae, the floor completely outside the court, any of the net or cables outside the antennae, the referee stand or pole, or the ceiling above a non-playable area.
- It is legal to contact the ball with any part of a player's body.
- It is illegal to catch, hold or throw the ball.

National and International Tournaments Associated With the Game

Most Important Volleyball Tournaments:

- Nations League
- Olympic Games
- World Championship
- World Cup
- European Championship
- Asian Championship
- African Championship
- South American Championship
- NORCECA Championship
- Club World Championship
- FIVB World Grand Prix
- FIVB World Grand Champions Cup
- CEV Champions League
- AVC Champions League
- Pan American Games
- Asian Games

Team/Individual records (World, Olympic, Asian and National Level) of the game

World Cup

Volleyball World Cup winners list: Men's

Year	Champions	Runners-Up
1965	Soviet Union	Poland
1969	East Germany	Japan
1977	Soviet Union	Japan
1981	Soviet Union	Cuba
1985	USA	Soviet Union
1989	Cuba	Italy
1991	Soviet Union	Cuba

1995	Italy	Netherlands
1999	Russia	Cuba
2003	Brazil	Italy
2007	Brazil	Russia
2011	Russia	Poland
2015	USA	Italy
2019	Brazil	Poland

Volleyball World Cup winners list: Women's

Year	Champions	Runners-Up
1973	Soviet Union	Japan
1977	Japan	Cuba
1981	China	Japan
1985	China	Cuba
1989	Cuba	Soviet Union
1991	Cuba	China
1995	Cuba	Brazil
1999	Cuba	Russia
2003	China	Brazil
2007	Italy	Brazil
2011	Italy	USA
2015	China	Serbia
2019	China	USA

Olympic Games

Men's Volleyball Winners at Olympics

Year	Gold	Silver	Bronze
1964	Soviet Union	Czechoslovakia	Japan
1968	Soviet Union	Japan	Czechoslovakia

1972	Japan	East Germany	Soviet Union
1976	Poland	Soviet Union	Cuba
1980	Soviet Union	Bulgaria	Romania
1984	United States	Brazil	Italy
1988	United States	Soviet Union	Argentina
1992	Brazil	Netherlands	United States
1996	Netherlands	Italy	Yugoslavia
2000	Yugoslavia	Russia	Italy
2004	Brazil	Italy	Russia
2008	United States	Brazil	Russia
2012	Russia	Brazil	Italy
2016	Brazil	Italy	United States

Women's Volleyball Winners at Olympics

Year	**Gold**	**Silver**	**Bronze**
1964	Japan	Soviet Union	Poland
1968	Soviet Union	Japan	Poland
1972	Soviet Union	Japan	North Korea
1976	Japan	Soviet Union	South Korea
1980	Soviet Union	East Germany	Bulgaria
1984	China	United States	Japan
1988	Soviet Union	Peru	China
1992	Cuba	Unified Team	United States
1996	Cuba	China	Brazil
2000	Cuba	Russia	Brazil
2004	China	Russia	Cuba
2008	Brazil	United States	China
2012	Brazil	United States	Japan
2016	China	Serbia	United States

Asian Games

Asian Games 2023 men's volleyball: Results and scores

Date	Match Result	Match Score	Stage	Venue
September 19, Tuesday	India 3-0 Cambodia	25-14, 25-13, 25-19	Pool C	CXC Gymnasium
September 20, Wednesday	India 3-2 Republic of Korea	25-27, 29-27, 25-22, 20-25, 17-15	Pool C	LSC Gymnasium
September 22, Friday	India 3-0 Chinese Taipei	25-22, 25-22, 25-21	Cross Match for Top 12	CXC Gymnasium
September 24, Sunday	India 0-3 Japan	16-25, 18-25, 17-25	Classification match 1-6	CXC Gymnasium
September 26, Tuesday	India 0-3 Pakistan	21-25, 20-25, 23-25	Classification match 5-6	CXC Gymnasium

Asian Games 2023 women's volleyball: Results and scores

Date	Match	Pool/Phase	Venue
September 30, Saturday	India 1-3 DPR Korea	A	DQ Sports Gymnasium
October 1, Sunday	India 0-3 China	A	DQ Sports Gymnasium
October 4, Wednesday	India 3-1 Nepal	Classificati on Pool G (9-13)	Hangzhou Normal University Cangqian Gymnasium
October 6, Friday	India 3-0 Mongolia	Classificati on 9th-12th	DQ Sports Gymnasium
October 7, Saturday	India 3-2 Hong Kong China	Classificati on 9th-10th	Hangzhou Normal University Cangqian Gymnasium

Awards Associated With the Game

- Arjuna Award
- Ekalavya Award
- Dronacharya Award
- Dhyan Chand Award
- Maulana Abul Kalam Azad (MAKA) Award
- Algerian Best Athlete of the Year

Duties of the Officials

- The referee initiates service, and controls the tempo of the game.
- The referee is primarily responsible for judgements regarding ball handling.
- The referee is only responsible for rotation of serving team.
- The referee has the duty of communication with umpire, captains and statistician.
- The referee performs the toss up from service and court.

Technical Equipment for Officiating

- Game clock and stop watch.
- 30 second devices
- Score sheet
- Whistles
- Score board
- Player foul marker
- Team foul marker.

Knowledge of the Score Sheets

Volleyball Score Sheet is used to record a point-by-point account of the match and individual statistics as well as service order. Official volleyball scoresheets are recorded by an official scorer, who must be good at it in a professional level, a coach or a parent at high school or club levels is much more likely to be chose to take that duty. To fill out a complex volleyball scorebook requires a strong concentration and a professional knowledge of the game. The analysis of the information included in the score sheet can tell you how many points you have won and lost in the different rotations of the games and matches.

Date:________ Home:________ Visitor:________ Site:________ Start Time:______ End Time:______

Game Number:________ Level (Varsity, JV or Freshmen):________________

Time-Outs			First Serve (check box below)		Time-Outs		
Serve Order	Player No.	Team			Serve Order	Player No.	Team:
1			1 16 2 17 3 18	1 16 2 17 3 18	1		
2			4 19 5 20	4 19 5 20	2		
3			6 21 7 22 8 23	6 21 7 22 8 23	3		
4			9 24 10 25	9 24 10 25	4		
5			11 26 12 27 13 28	11 26 12 27 13 28	5		
6			14 29 15 30	14 29 15 30	6		

Official Verification

Subs: 1 2 3 4 5 6 7 8 9 10 11 12 13 14 15 16 17 18 **Subs:** 1 2 3 4 5 6 7 8 9 10 11 12 13 14 15 16 17 18

Comments: ________________ Comments: ________________

Referee ________ (Print) ________ (Signature) **Umpire** ________ (Print) ________ (Signature)

Scorekeeper ________ (Print)

Key: c=Playing Captain 1=Point – =Loss of Rally P1=Penalty Point R=Replay RS=Re-Serve S=Substitution Sx=Opponent Substitution T=Time-out Tx=Opponent Time-out =Action as Result of No Serve

If the receiving team wins the rally, it receives a point which is recorded on the line of the **NEXT** server's number and a square is drawn around it. **Also** draw a square around the same point on the team's running score.

Signals of Officiating

UNIT-II

General Warming-Up

The general warm-up should consist of a light physical activity, like walking, jogging, easy swimming, stationary bike riding, skipping or easy aerobics. Both the intensity and duration of the general warm-up (or how hard and how long), should be governed by the fitness level of the participating athlete. To begin your warm-up do 5 minutes of light (low intensity) physical activity such as walking, jogging on the spot or on a trampoline, or cycling. Pump your arms or make large but controlled circular movements with your arms to help warm the muscles of your upper body.

Specific Warming-Up

In this type of warm-up specific types of exercises are performed after the activities of general warm-up. Specific type of warming-up differs from activity to activity. A specific warm-up is when you focus on just the areas of your body you are working on that day. So if you are working on increasing your speed on the track one day, you design your specific warm-up to support that goal.

Cooling Down

A cool down is designed to promote recovery and return the body to a pre-exercise or pre-workout level. This can be accomplished in a variety of different ways. You can walk or jog, stretch, or even engage in mindfulness to help your body relax and recover. Whether physical or mental activities or a combination of both a cool down helps you recover mentally and physically after physical activity or exercise. Cooling down after your workout lets the heart rate and blood pressure slowly recover to preexercise levels. It may be most important for competitive endurance athletes, such as marathoners, to cool down to help control blood flow. Cooling down doesn't seem to help reduce muscle stiffness and soreness after exercise, but more research is needed. A cool down eases you out of your workout and allows your heart rate and breathing to gradually return to normal.

Long-term and short-term preparation for the decisive volleyball competitions

To compete as a top athlete, you must be quick on your feet, flexible enough for high jumps, and possess a good amount of strength. Athletes devote many hours of training over a season with a support team consisting of coaches, trainers and doctors to ultimately get the chance to compete at their highest levels. Preparation can be a deciding factor in whether an athlete is ready to perform well. This makes preparation one of the important keys to realizing their potential. Sometimes a match is won even before it starts due to an athlete's high level of preparation. Proper breathing techniques can help manage stress and anxiety, which are common in competitive sports like volleyball. Practice deep breathing exercises to calm your mind and relax your body. Before a game or during breaks, take deep, controlled breaths to center yourself and reduce tension.

Psychological Qualities and Preparation of a Volleyball Player

Concentration and Focus

Volleyball requires intense concentration and focus throughout the game. Players need to pay attention to the movements of the ball, their teammates, and opponents. Maintaining focus is crucial for quick decision-making and executing skills effectively.

Tactical Awareness

Volleyball involves strategic thinking and tactical awareness. Players must anticipate the actions of their opponents, read the game situation, and make split-second decisions. This demand requires the ability to analyze and adapt to changing circumstances on the court.

Mindfulness and Meditation

Mindfulness and meditation are excellent practices for improving concentration and mental clarity. Regular meditation can help you stay present during the game, allowing you to react more effectively to the play. Mindfulness involves being aware of the moment, which is crucial in a fast-paced game like volleyball. Incorporating these practices into your daily routine can significantly enhance your mental resilience, both in structured matches and in the spontaneous nature of drop-in volleyball. They help you maintain focus amidst distractions and remain calm under pressure, which is invaluable for any volleyball player.

Create a Pre-game Ritual

Athletes prepare for volleyball matches differently. Volleyball players listen to their favourite songs, visualize, meditate and do other activities that help them mentally prepare for a game and achieve the success on the court. Once you start participating in volleyball competitions, you'll be able to test different mental training techniques. Sooner or later, you'll be able to develop your own pre-game ritual.

Communication and Teamwork

Volleyball is a team sport that heavily relies on effective communication and teamwork. Players must communicate with their teammates through verbal and non-verbal cues to coordinate movements, execute plays, and maintain team cohesion. Strong communication skills and the ability to work collaboratively are essential for success.

Offensive, Defense System in Play

Offensive and defensive strategies in defense refer to the actions taken by individuals involved in a game or conflict situation. The goal of attackers is to disrupt the current state of affairs, while defenders aim to protect the system and maintain stability. Attackers may employ tactics like malicious code attacks and denial of service attacks, whereas defenders can utilize defensive strategies such as web services security strategy defense and code reconstruction defense. Achieving success in both aspects of the conflict is generally easier in the defensive realm, as defense strategies focus on repelling attacks, deterring through punishment, and assertive disarmament. The choice of offensive and defensive strategies depends on various factors, including the environment, the actions of the attacker, and the differing perceptions of the players.

Service and Reception Pattern

1. Server throws balls to the passer.
2. Passer, digs up to the setter, setter catches it and roles it under the net.
3. Server throws with one arm and repeats process.
4. Server, serves over normally and repeats process.
5. Server bounces the ball and jumps serves and repeats process.

Individual, Group and Team Tactics

Team tactics refer to the coordinated strategies, plans, and actions that a group of individuals employ to achieve specific goals or objectives. A group is a collection of individuals who coordinate their efforts, while a team is a group of people who share a common goal. While similar, the two are different when it comes to decision-making and teamwork. There are many tactics for attacking. When the opponent is playing perimeter defense, tip the ball to the middle of the court. If your setter plays across the front row, rather than setting one of the other two front row attackers, the setter could attack the 2nd ball. The best teams design plays. If you're opponent is slower at the net blocking, run a faster play. A quick set to the middle or shoot to the outside will make it difficult for the opponent to get in position to block.

Diet and Nutrition for a Volleyball Player

While nutrition on the court on match day is important, a healthy eating pattern off the court will provide an essential base for a fit, fast and lean volleyball player.

A daily intake for a player should be based around nutrient rich carbohydrates, (grainy breads, brown rice, quinoa, wholemeal pasta); lean protein sources, (lean red meat, poultry, seafood, eggs, dairy and lentils) and healthy fat sources, (avocado, olive oil, nuts and fish); as well as fruit and plenty vegetables. A well-balanced diet is important for each volleyball player to ensure you'll meet your nutritional needs and help improve training and performance outcomes. Hydration is a vital aspect of sports nutrition, especially in a physically demanding sport like volleyball. Staying adequately hydrated before, during, and after playing is essential.

Coordination among the Manager, Coach, Doctor, Psychologist and Players

Coordination also allows for the more beneficial and efficient allocation of resources in an organization, which can reduce conflict and redundancies between individuals or departments. Coordination is the body's ability to perform smooth and efficient movements. Good coordination requires the athlete to combine multiple movements into a single movement that is fluid and achieves the intended goal. This is contrary to what many people first think of, which is hand-eye coordination which refers to the relationship between eye movements and hand movements, so that our hands make an intended movement in response to our eye movement, usually tracking a ball or something similar.

UNIT-III

Teaching of Volleyball Skills

The six basic volleyball skills are:-

1. Passing
2. Setting
3. Spiking
4. Blocking
5. Digging
6. Serving

Preparing a Lesson Plan

Creating a lesson plan begins with aligning state standards to your curriculum and then narrowing the focus to determine which objectives you want your students to meet within a specific unit of study. Strong lesson plans are the foundation of an efficient classroom environment for both the teacher and the students. A lesson plan is the instructor's road map of what students need to learn and how it will be done effectively during the class time. Before you plan your lesson, you will first need to identify the learning objectives.

Specific Training Methods for Different Playing Positions

Your coaches will cover skills such as:

- Hand and body positioning
- Movement and footwork to ball: move stop set, square to four on front and back set
- Repetition, repetition, repetition!
- Jump setting
- Bad ball setting
- Variety of sets high balls to variety of quick's
- Second ball attack dump with left and right hand, dump when off the net
- Blocking hand position, penetration, positioning and timing

- Play calling off serve receive and in transition
- Running an effective offense
- Setting against the flow

Athletes should develop basic volleyball skills such as hitting, passing, setting, digging and blocking. However, volleyball training also depends on player's position on the court. There are volleyball workouts that work well for every athlete. Functional training stands out as an exceptional method that can effectively enhance various aspects of volleyball players' performance, such as sensitivity, jumping ability, lower limb explosive power, core strength, back strength, coordination ability, and speed. This approach breaks from traditional training paradigms, proposing innovative, specific power for the contemporary physical training method. Volleyball techniques are intricate and require specific physical conditioning. For instance, the volleyball smash technique has seen significant improvement through functional training. However, certain shortcomings exist in the practical application of functional training in volleyball coaching and training, which warrant careful attention in future teaching processes.

Counselling During Competitions

A sport counsellor teaches an athlete to visualize successfully completing a certain action in sporting activity. This will give the athlete confidence to complete the maneuver as well as prepare the athletes body for the actual maneuver.

- Building and sustaining ideal level of motivation.
- Helping to achieve optimum level of self-Confidence.
- Enhancing Focus and concentration while dealing with distractions.
- Inculcating positivity and reducing negative self-talk.
- Managing competitive stress and anxiety.
- Building commitment towards one's sport and setting goals.
- Improving Team building and communication.
- Replacing fear of failure with desire to succeed.
- Managing and channelizing anger and negative emotions.
- Dealing with competitive pressure.
- Working on positive sport parenting.

Information and Publicity of the Competition

Publicity is a way of creating media attention on a service, product, or business by writing commercially important information on it in the media and not paying for time or space directly. Publicity adds credibility, has more data, is cost-effective, and is faster. Sports public relations is promoting teams, individual players and sports organizations through earned media channels including broadcast, print, radio, and online media outlets. Most colleges have many sports teams, and larger colleges may require multiple sports information directors to cover all of their teams. Typically, one sports information director may handle all information for all the sports for a college. This means that a sports information director should understand and appreciate most if not all sports. Since they work with sports in each season, it also means they work throughout the year but may have a break during the summer if they work at a college or high school.

Writing Press Release and Reports

A press release is an official statement (written or recorded) that an organization issues to the news media and beyond. A press release is a written communication distributed to members of the media with the primary purpose of announcing news, events, or information about a business, organization, or individual. A sports press release helps you share your story and let the world know what your sports event is all about, what makes it different and your visions as well. You can write a great press release by following a template or using a press release sample. The purpose of a sporting event press release is to inform the media, fans, and potential attendees about the event while generating anticipation and interest. A press release written for your sporting event can help you generate media attention giving you quick traction and brand trust as well.

Facility Management

Facilities management can be defined as the tools and services that support the functionality, safety, and sustainability of buildings, grounds, infrastructure, and real estate. Facilities managers help businesses optimize their workspaces to allow for function and safety while seeking opportunities to reduce costs. Working in facilities management can be a rewarding career with opportunities to advance to a manager or director position. Sport facilities can range from gyms and park and recreation departments to large arenas and stadiums. A Sport Facility Manager is responsible for managing and maintaining sport and recreation facilities. Sport facility management is the set of activities concerning the management and maintenance of sport facilities. Sports Facility Management involves a variety of tasks, such as budgeting, staffing, marketing, and customer service. It also includes the development and implementation of policies and procedures to ensure the safety and security of the facility and its patrons.

Quality Control of Equipment and Player's Kit

Quality control is a procedure or set of procedures intended to ensure that a manufactured product or performed service adheres to a defined set of quality criteria or meets the requirements of the client or customer. Quality control is essential for any company that manufactures products or provides a service. It helps improve customer satisfaction by consistently delivering quality products or services, reduce wastage of resources and increase efficiency and profits for the company.

Key components of Quality Control may include:

Testing
Conducting various tests and measurements to assess the performance, functionality, or characteristics of products or services.

Inspection
Regularly examining products, materials, or services to identify defects, non-compliance, or deviations from quality standards.

Statistical Process Control
Employing statistical techniques to monitor and control the production processes, ensuring that they remain within acceptable quality limits.

Corrective Action
Implementing appropriate measures to address any identified quality issues and prevent their recurrence.

Training and Education
Providing employees with the necessary skills and knowledge to maintain quality standards effectively.

Continuous Improvement
Constantly analyzing data and feedback to identify areas for improvement and enhancing the overall quality management system.

Documentation and Records
Keeping detailed records of inspections, tests, and corrective actions taken to maintain traceability and accountability.

Risk Management

Risk management is the process of identifying, assessing and controlling financial, legal, strategic and security risks to an organization's capital and earnings. Risk management is the set of steps an organization takes to prevent unwanted events from happening, or at least to reduce the damage of those events when they do happen. Effective risk management means attempting to control, as much as possible, future outcomes by acting proactively rather than reactively. Therefore, effective risk management offers the potential to reduce both the possibility of a risk occurring and its potential impact. Risk management is the systematic process of identifying, assessing, and mitigating threats or uncertainties that can affect your organization.

Medical Check-Up

Regular health check-ups can identify any early signs of health issues. Finding problems early means that your chances for effective treatment are increased. Many factors, such as your age, health, family history and lifestyle choices, impact on how often you need check-ups. A general medical check-up is a complete health evaluation by a physician or a nurse practitioner. It checks your overall health, determines if you have any health problems, and helps you understand what you can do to improve your health. A physical exam is an evaluation of your overall health. A primary care provider performs a physical exam. This exam focuses on preventive care so you can get to good health or maintain it. If your provider suspects a health concern or you have a concern, they may refer you to see a specialist or offer tests to learn more about your symptoms. You don't have to be ill to get a physical exam.

Medical Aid and Insurance

Medical aid covers members' healthcare costs such as hospitalisation, treatments and medicine. These costs are covered according to the rules of the medical scheme and the member's medical aid plan type. Health insurance provides several benefits. It offers financial protection by covering a significant portion of medical expenses. It ensures access to top-quality healthcare services at private facilities, including preventive care, screenings, check-ups, and treatments, which improve overall health, and early disease detection. Health insurance is an insurance product which covers medical and surgical expenses of an insured individual. It reimburses the expenses incurred due to illness or injury or pays the care provider of the insured individual directly.

Personnel Management

Personnel management is an administrative function within an organization that oversees the hiring, organization and support of employee positions. Personnel management deals with the managerial function of estimating and classifying human resources requirements for meeting organizational goals through people at work and their relationships with each other. A branch of human resources, personnel management focuses on recruiting the right individuals to fit a position and supporting those already working for the company. This area also functions as a tool for evaluating the hiring process and gaining insight into employee satisfaction. Personnel management is defined as an administrative specialization that focuses on hiring and developing employees to become more valuable to the company. It is sometimes considered to be a sub-category of human resources that only focuses on administration.

Interpersonal Communication Skills

Interpersonal communication is the process of exchange of information, ideas and feelings between two or more people through verbal or non-verbal methods. Face-to-face communication often involves hearing, seeing, and feeling body language, facial expressions, and gestures. In other terms,

Interpersonal communication is exchanging information, meaning, feelings, and opinions between two or more people via verbal and non-verbal means. Interpersonal skills involve the ability to communicate and build relationships with others. Often called 'people skills', they tend to incorporate both your innate personality traits and how you have learned to handle certain social situations.

UNIT-IV

Injuries associated with the game:-

Ankle sprain

A sprained ankle is an injury that occurs when you roll, twist or turn your ankle in an awkward way. This can stretch or tear the tough bands of tissue (ligaments) that help hold your ankle bones together. An ankle sprain occurs when the strong ligaments that support the ankle stretch beyond their limits and tear. The severity of a sprain can vary greatly depending on the number of ligaments involved and the extent to which the ligaments are torn. A sprained ankle is when the ligaments in your ankle are torn. A broken ankle or ankle fracture is when one or more of the bones in your ankle break. Severe sprains and fractures have similar symptoms (pain, swelling, bruising, and tenderness) and are both caused by twisting or rotating your ankle, tripping or falling, or trauma to your ankle. Sprains heal faster, but it can take up to six weeks for a broken ankle to heal.

Finger injuries

Finger and hand injuries are common among athletes. Hand and finger injuries occur most often in contact sports, such as those that involve catching a ball or using hand equipment like ski poles or common sports, like basketball and volleyball. They also occur in high-speed sports like skating and biking. Finger injuries range from minor cuts and scrapes to wounds with significant damage to bone, tendons, and ligaments. If not treated properly, serious finger injuries can lead to permanent deformity and loss of function. Careful treatment allows for a faster and more complete recovery.

Shoulder Dislocation

A dislocated shoulder is an injury in which the upper arm bone pops out of the cup-shaped socket that's part of the shoulder blade. The shoulder is the body's most flexible joint, which makes it more likely to dislocate. Dislocations happen when something pushes the bones in your shoulder joint out of their usual place. Shoulder dislocation can happen to anyone

and can be caused by trauma to the shoulder through sports injuries, falls or other accidents in which the shoulder is forced out of place. Shoulder dislocation can also occur as a result of overuse from repetitive activities or from previous dislocations that loosen connective tissues that keep the humerus in place within the socket.

Knee displacement

Kneecap dislocation occurs when the round-shaped bone covering the knee (patella) moves or slides out of place. The dislocation often occurs toward the outside of the leg. A dislocated knee is when the three bones of your knee are out of place and aren't aligned the way they should be. It can happen if the structures in your knee are abnormal. Some people are born with a knee dislocation (congenital dislocation of the knee). Most of the time, knee dislocations happen when a traumatic event thrusts the bones in your knee joint out of place with great force. It's an emergency, and it's very painful.

Preventive and Safety Measures

Stretching exercises

Stretching exercises can improve the ability of muscles to contract and perform, reducing the risk for injury. Each stretch should start slowly until you reach a point of muscle tension. Stretching should not be painful. Aim to hold each stretch for up to 20 seconds.

Wear the right gear

Players should wear appropriate and properly fit protective equipment such as pads (neck, shoulder, elbow, chest, knee, and shin), helmets, mouthpieces, face guards, protective cups, and eyewear. Young athletes should not assume that protective gear will prevent all injuries while performing more dangerous or risky activities.

Provide a healthy, well-balanced diet

It's important for athletes to eat a well-balanced diet full of fruits, vegetables and lean proteins, and to maintain a regular eating schedule. For instance, have breakfast, lunch and dinner around the same time each day. A poor diet that is high in processed foods and sugar can contribute to muscle weakness and decreased cardiovascular endurance. Hydration is equally important and should be maintained before, during, and after your workouts using water and electrolytes.

Cool Down

This is the most commonly forgotten portion of the workout. It helps safely bring the body, heart rate, and muscles back to their resting state. Perform 5-10 minutes of low-intensity cardiovascular activity, followed by stretching. Cooling down immediately after your workout will help decrease delayed onset muscle soreness and aid in recovery which will help prepare your body for its next workout.

Don't Play When You're Injured

This is a really important one. If you love sports, it's tempting to get right back in the game, even after an injury. But playing when you're hurt or before an injury has had a chance to fully heal is a bad idea. It can lead to an even worse injury, one that might side-line you for a long time.

Resume activity slowly

Don't be tempted to nurse your injury for too long. Excessive rest may delay healing. After the initial 48-hour period of RICE, you can start using heat to help relax tight muscles. Take things slowly, and ease back in to exercise or your sport of choice.

Maintain flexibility

It is extremely important that you do dynamic stretches before starting your activity. Cold muscles are more prone to injury, so, while it may be tempting to start playing immediately, you should take a few minutes to do some jumping jacks, butt kicks, or arm circles first.

P.R.I.C.E.

Protection, Rest, Ice, Compression and Elevation, or P.R.I.C.E., adds the concept of "protection" to the traditional R.I.C.E. protocol formula.

Protecting the injured area from further damage is crucial to the healing process. Protect the injured person and the area being treated but also protect yourself. If the injury occurs on the sports field, stop the game.

Rehabilitation and Physiotherapy

Rehabilitation is care that can help you get back, keep, or improve abilities that you need for daily life. Physiotherapy helps through physical rehabilitation, injury prevention, and health and fitness. Physiotherapists get you involved in your own recovery. The terms "physiotherapy" and "physical therapy" mean the same thing and are used interchangeably, as are the terms “physiotherapist” and “physical therapist”. Physiotherapists have in-depth knowledge of how the body works and specialized hands-on clinical skills to assess, diagnose, and treat symptoms of illness, injury and disability. Physiotherapy is treatment to restore, maintain, and make the most of a patient’s mobility, function, and well-being. Physiotherapists work with clients of all ages and with a wide range of health conditions. Whether its pain management and rehabilitation from an acute injury like a sprained ankle or management of chronic conditions such as diabetes or heart disease, a physiotherapist can help. Physical therapy is provided by physical therapists who promote, maintain or restore the wellbeing through examination, diagnosis, prognosis, patient education, physiotherapeutic intervention, rehabilitation, disease prevention and health promotion.

Training Means for Development of Different Components of Physical Fitness

Speed

Speed in physical education is one of the most important fitness components, whether one plays sports or not, everyone wants speed because actions in everyday life situations need to be carried out at the appropriate speed to be able to achieve success. Speed has a direct relationship with the nervous system and the muscular system. Speed in physical education is considered a physical component. The brain and nervous system control and coordinate the movements of our muscles. Speed is defined as the ability to move the body in one direction as fast as possible. Speed is one of the main fitness components, important for success in many sports. Speed is important in sprinting, speed skating, sprint cycling and sports such as tennis when a player has to move forward quickly from the baseline to reach a drop shot close to the net.

Strength

Strength is one of the main fitness components, important for success in many sports. Certain sports, such as weight lifting, wrestling and weight throwing, it is the most important physical attribute. A strength exercise is any activity that makes your muscles work harder than usual. This increases your muscles' strength, size, power and endurance. The activities involve using your body weight or working against a resistance. Strength is the ability of a muscle to exert force in single muscle contraction or it is the ability to overcome resistance. Strength is an essential component of physical fitness. Strength refers to the quality or state of being strong. Our muscles are vital to our bodies and are the reasons we can walk, run, carry things, and so much more. But muscles start to deteriorate as we age, so finding ways such as resistance training to build muscle is crucial.

Endurance

Endurance is defined as the ability to continue despite fatigue or difficult conditions. The stamina to perform physical activities for longer periods of time can be improved by exercise and increasing the amount of activity. Endurance refers to an individual's ability to sustain physical activity or mental effort over an extended period. It is the capacity to withstand fatigue, stress, and discomfort while maintaining optimal performance levels. Endurance is a crucial aspect of athletic performance and overall fitness, enabling athletes to compete and excel in various sports. Endurance is the capacity of a person to work in unpleasant and hard situation without giving up. In physical education, endurance is explained as the capacity to work against fatigue. Endurance refers to your body's physical capability to sustain an exercise for an extended period. It's made up of two components: cardiovascular endurance and muscular endurance. Cardiovascular endurance is the ability of your heart and lungs to fuel your body with oxygen. Muscular endurance is the ability of your muscles to work continuously without getting tired.

Flexibility

Flexibility is an important part of physical fitness and is defined as the ability to move the joints freely. Both range of motion and mobility are common terms when discussing flexibility. Range of motion is how much a joint or body part can move and mobility is how easy it is to move. Flexibility can be assessed using various methods depending on the specific joints or muscle groups being evaluated. Flexibility helps performance, posture, promotes efficient movement, prevents incorrect body alignment, maintains appropriate muscle length and balance and also decreases injury risk. Flexibility is the ability to move muscles and joints through a full normal range of motion. Flexibility refers to the ability of muscles, joints, and soft tissues to move through an unrestricted, pain-free range of motion. It involves the capacity of these structures to stretch, lengthen, and contract without limitations, allowing for smooth and efficient movement.

Co-coordinative Abilities

Coordination is understood, in general terms, as the ability of the human body to unify in a synchronised manner the work of various muscles in the execution of an intentional action. Gross motor coordination involves the large muscles in your arms, legs, and torso, which you use for everyday activities like walking, lifting, throwing, running, and kicking. Fine motor coordination focuses on coordination of the small muscles in your hands and wrists the ones you use to write, type on your computer or phone, or do activities like sewing. Hand/eye coordination is the coordination of the information your eyes take in, and the signals your brain sends to your arms and hands. You rely on this to do everyday tasks like drive a car, cook, or pick up something. Coordination is the ability to select the right muscle at the right time with proper intensity to achieve proper action. Coordinated movement is characterized by appropriate speed, distance, direction, timing and muscular tension. Coordination is about our motor skills and can be broken up into fine or gross motor skills. Fine motor skills are about our coordination in relation to small movements and the ease they are performed. An example of a fine motor skill in sport is the snooker shot. Conversely, gross motor skills involve large movements and muscle groups. Examples of gross motor skills include walking, kicking, jumping and much more.

Practical Course

Course Code: PED302PR

Specialization in Football

UNIT-I

History of Game

Football is a team sport in which two teams play against each other to score their spherical ball in the other opponents net (what we call a 'goal'). Both teams usually have 11 players in different positions on the pitch. Each positions main aim is to keep the opposing team from scoring a goal in their net. It's a strategic game and requires tenacity and skill. Players also tackle and battle to get the ball from opposing teams to overall try and score a goal for themselves.

Football is an American sport that was formed in the late 1800's at college campuses. The sport has its roots in the English game of Rugby. The first college game was played between Rutgers and Princeton. This early form of football was extremely violent with many players actually dying every year. New rules were established over time and, although football is still a physical sport with many injuries, it is much safer today. The NFL was formed in 1921 and became the major professional league by the 50's. It has continued to grow in popularity becoming the most watched professional league of any sport in the United States. The aim of football is to score more goals then your opponent in a 90 minute playing time frame. The match is split up into two halves of 45 minutes. After the first 45 minutes players will take a 15 minute rest period called half time. The second 45 minutes will resume and any time deemed fit to be added on by the referee (injury time) will be accordingly.

Measurement and Preparation of the Play Field

The field of play is rectangular and marked with lines called boundary lines. The two longer boundary lines are touch lines and the two shorter lines are goal lines. It is divided into two halves by a halfway line, which joins the midpoints of the two touch lines. The centre mark is at the midpoint of the halfway line.

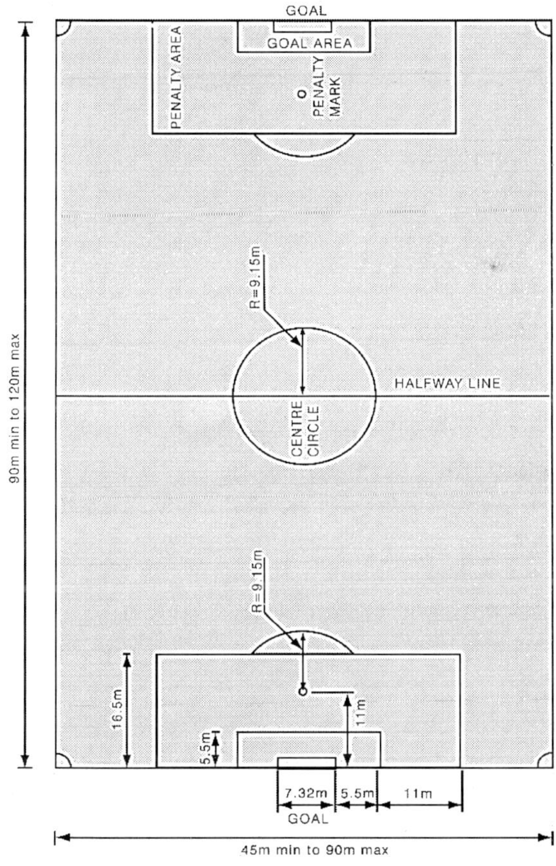

A circle with a radius of 9.15m is marked around it. Marks are made off the field of play, 9.15m from the corner arc and at right angles to the goal lines and the touch lines, to ensure defending players retreat this distance when a corner kick is taken. The length of the touch line is greater than the length of the goal line. All lines are not more than 12cm wide. During a game, players are only allowed to wear soccer equipment and are prohibited to wear anything that may harm him as well as the other. This includes any kind of jewellery and other accessories.

Equipment Required for Game

Ball

A Football is made of vulcanized rubber with plastic bladders and covered by plastic covers. This the main equipment of the game and the total game revolves around this.

Shin Guards

These are used to protect the player's shin. While playing football, opponent players try to injure players by kicking in the shin area. It could be an intentional or unintentional act by the player. Hence, shin guards are a protective equipment.

Fundamental Skills and Lead-Up Games

Passing and receiving

These two basic tools are the most essential ingredients for any footballer's success. Accuracy is the key when it comes to passing and receiving. It makes open play fluid and ensures constant progress up the field that can result in creating scoring opportunities.

Dribbling Skills

The most important and fundamental skill in football is being able to dribble the ball while keeping possession of it. It's not as simple as it may seem to run with the ball; it demands good control, balance, and coordination.

Tackling

Football games are not as easy to understand as they would seem to spectators. To get the ball and kick it toward the goal, players must use a range of techniques and tactics on the field.

Techniques, Strategies and Method of Play

The most efficient and basic skill for football is to dribble the ball, keeping it in possession. Running with the ball is not as simple as it sounds because it needs good control, balance, and coordination. To get a grab on it, move up and down the pitch with the ball in possession and maintain your control.

Rules and Regulations of the Game

- There should be 11 eleven players in each team. Out of 11, one must be the goalie. A team must have at least seven players in order to be considered complete. The players should hit the ball with either their legs or torso. No player is permitted to use their hands or arms to touch the ball, except the goalkeepers.
- All players must use their feet head or chest to play the ball. Only the goalkeeper is allowed to use their hands, and only within their designated goal area.
- The aim of the game is to score a goal, which is achieved by kicking or heading the ball into the opposition team's goal.
- If the ball completely crosses the side line, it is thrown back in by the team that was not the last to touch the ball.
- The game is controlled by a central referee, and two linesmen. They award free kicks and penalties when rules are broken. For continual breaking of rules or for a bad foul, the player may shown a red card and be sent off.
- The objective of Football or Soccer is to score goals by kicking or passing the ball over the goal line and into the opponent's goalposts. A goal is said to have been scored, if the ball crosses the goal line, between the goalposts, and under the crossbar, provided that no offence has been committed by the scoring team.
- A goal is scored when the entire ball has crossed the goal line within the frame of the goal. At the end of the match, the team with the most goals is the winner, barring the circumstantial necessity for extra time.
- A goal kick is awarded when the offensive team plays the ball out of bounds over the defensive team's goal line. After the ball is out of play, the defender or goalkeeper may place the ball

anywhere within the six-yard goal box and kick the ball back into play.

- A referee is an official who oversees a game. They have the last say in all matters, including disputes. They have the power to penalize a player, stop a match in case of a foul and have the general responsibility to oversee the game so that it goes without a hitch.

National and International Tournaments Associated With the Game

Most Important Soccer Tournaments:-

- World Cup
- UEFA Champions League
- UEFA European Championship
- Copa America
- AFC Asian Cup
- FIFA Club World Cup
- UEFA Europa League
- FA Cup (England)
- Bundesliga (Germany)
- Premier League (England)
- La Liga (Spain)
- Serie A (Italy)
- Ligue 1 (France)
- Major League Soccer (United States)
- Eredivisie (The Netherlands)

Team/Individual records (World, Olympic, Asian and National Level) of the Game

World Championships

Most FIFA Men's World Cup wins

Country	Titles	Year
Brazil	5	1958, 1962 1970, 1994, 2002
Germany	4	1954, 1974, 1990, 2014

Italy	4	1934, 1938, 1982, 2006
Argentina	3	1978, 1986, 2022
France	2	1998, 2018
Uruguay	2	1930, 1950
England	1	1966
Spain	1	2010

Most FIFA Women's World Cup wins

Country	**Titles**	**Year**
USA	4	1991, 1999, 2015, 2019
Germany	2	2003, 2007
Norway	1	1995
Japan	1	2011

Olympic Games

List of Men's Olympic football records

Record	**Holders**
Most Games participated	Italy (15)
Most gold medals	Hungary (3)
Most medals	Brazil (7)
Best performance by a host nation	Great Britain, Belgium, Spain, Brazil (Champions)
Most goals scored in a match	Denmark's bt France 17-1 at London 1908
Biggest margin of victory	Denmark bt France 17-1 (London 1908); Germany bt Russian Empire 16-0 (Stockholm 1912)
Highest goal scorer (overall)	Antal Dunai (13)
Highest goal scorer (single edition)	Ferenc Bene (12)
Highest goal scorer in a match	Gottfried Fuchs (10)

Youngest goal-scorer	Ángel Uribe (PER) vs France at Rome 1960 - 16 years, 332 days
Oldest goal-scorer	Ryan Giggs (GBR) vs UAE at London 2012 - 38 years, 243 days

List of Women's Olympic football records

Record	**Holder**
Most Games participated	Brazil, Sweden, USA (6)
Most gold medals	USA (4)
Most medals	USA (6)
Best performance by a host nation	USA (Champions)
Most goals scored in a match	Netherlands bt Zambia 10-3 at Tokyo 2020
Biggest margin of victory	Germany bt China 8-0 at Athens 2004
Highest goal scorer (overall)	Cristiane (14)
Highest goal scorer (single edition)	Vivianne Miedema (NED) -- 10 goals at Tokyo 2020
Highest goal scorer in a match	Birgit Prinz and Vivianne Miedema (4)
Youngest goal-scorer	Ellie Carpenter (AUS) vs Zimbabwe at Rio 2016 - 16 years, 119 days
Oldest goal-scorer	Formiga (BRA) vs Netherlands at Tokyo 2020 - 43 years, 143 days

Asian Games

Indian football team results at Asian Games

Edition	**Medal/position**
New Delhi 1951	Gold (1st)
Manila 1954	8th
Tokyo 1958	4th

Jakarta 1962	Gold (1st)
Bangkok 1966	8th
Bangkok 1970	Bronze (3rd)
Tehran 1974	13th
Bangkok 1978	8th
New Delhi 1982	6th
Seoul 1986	16th
Beijing 1990	Did not play
Hiroshima 1994	Did not play
Bangkok 1998	16th
Busan 2002	10th
Doha 2006	14th
Guangzhou 2010	14th
Incheon 2014	26th
Jakarta 2018	Did not play
Hangzhou 2023	9th

Awards Associated With the Game

- FIFA World Player of the Year
- UEFA Men's Player of the Year Award
- FIFA World Cup Golden Ball
- CAF Player of the Year
- The European Golden Shoe
- FIFA Puskas Award
- FIFA World Coach of the Year
- Golden Boy Award
- Golden Glove

Duties of the Officials

- Football officials enforce the rules of the game and, as such, are usually the people who draw the most ire from coaches, players and fans.

- Without these rule keepers monitoring the progress of a football game, the game might not progress with a set structure.
- There are seven officials in football and they each have very important roles. Officials keep the game rolling along by monitoring the game clock and play clock.
- They also call a penalty when a rule is broken, record all rule infractions and make sure the athletes do not unnecessarily hurt each other.

Technical Equipment for Officiating

- Game clock and stop watch.
- 30 second devices
- Score sheet
- Whistles
- Score board
- Player foul marker
- Team foul marker.

Knowledge of the Score Sheets

In general, the scoresheet is the official record of the result of the game.

SOCCER LEAGUE
OFFI CI AL SCORESHEET

Date: .... Referee: ....

Venue: .... Final Score: .... for .... (School)

Team Roster for: .... Home/ Visitor (Circle one)

Player No.	Player Name	Scoring		Cards
		1st	2nd	

Coach:

Signals of Officiating

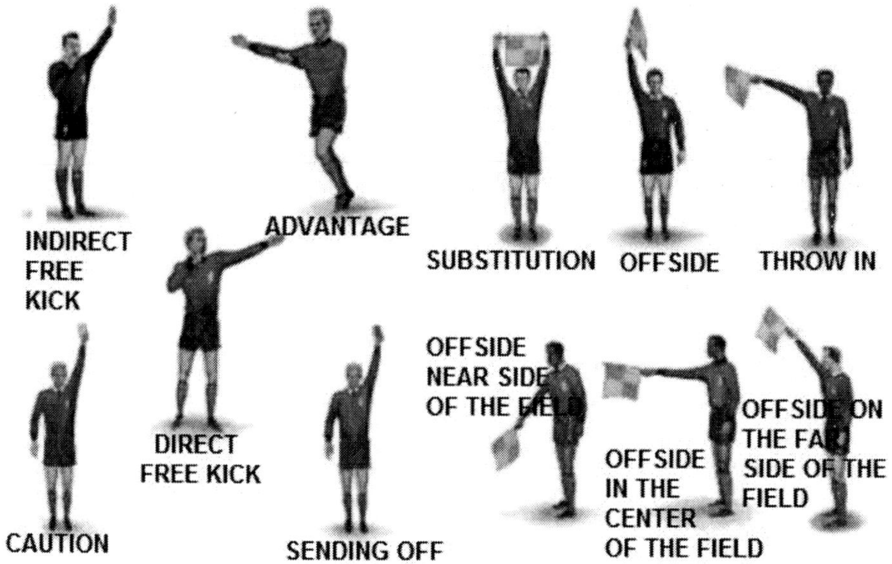

UNIT-II

General Warming-Up

The general warm-up should consist of a light physical activity, like walking, jogging, easy swimming, stationary bike riding, skipping or easy aerobics. Both the intensity and duration of the general warm-up (or how hard and how long), should be governed by the fitness level of the participating athlete. To begin your warm-up do 5 minutes of light (low intensity) physical activity such as walking, jogging on the spot or on a trampoline, or cycling. Pump your arms or make large but controlled circular movements with your arms to help warm the muscles of your upper body.

Specific Warming-Up

In this type of warm-up specific types of exercises are performed after the activities of general warm-up. Specific type of warming-up differs from activity to activity. A specific warm-up is when you focus on just the areas of your body you are working on that day. So if you are working on increasing your speed on the track one day, you design your specific warm-up to support that goal.

Cooling Down

A cool down is designed to promote recovery and return the body to a pre-exercise or pre-workout level. This can be accomplished in a variety of different ways. You can walk or jog, stretch, or even engage in mindfulness to help your body relax and recover. Whether physical or mental activities or a combination of both a cool down helps you recover mentally and physically after physical activity or exercise. Cooling down after your workout lets the heart rate and blood pressure slowly recover to preexercise levels. It may be most important for competitive endurance athletes, such as marathoners, to cool down to help control blood flow. Cooling down doesn't seem to help reduce muscle stiffness and soreness after exercise, but more research is needed. A cool down eases you out of your workout and allows your heart rate and breathing to gradually return to normal.

Long-term and Short-Term Preparation for the Decisive Football Competitions

The Preparatory Period, commonly known as the pre-season, aims to contribute to the acquisition of sporting form through the development of elementary factors in the physiological, tactical-technical and psychological domains. This is the key period for getting the players and team in the right physical condition. This phase should last between 4 and 10 weeks (depending on the level of the players and the level of competition participating in) and must consider physiological factors also. Inevitably, specific skills relevant to the sport will also be developed during training sessions, but the following methods of training develop the physical components of fitness.

Psychological Qualities and Preparation of a Football Player

The psychological preparation plays a particularly important role, being meant to group the player's resources and skills that allow him to process the information, select the answers and apply his tactic thinking, according to the game plan and game strategy formulated by the coach. The planning of the mental preparation is enforced by concretely establishing the objectives, actions, achievement means, responsible factors, related duties and by a current and periodical control of the results. Mental preparation should be a part of your regular warm up routine. You want to approach competition in the same way, no matter the significance of the game. Consistent mental preparation leads to consistent performance. Football is a sport that requires physical and technical skills, but in the pursuit of being a high performance player, mental preparation is of necessary importance.

Offensive, Defense System in Play

Offensive and defensive strategies in defense refer to the actions taken by individuals involved in a game or conflict situation. The goal of attackers is to disrupt the current state of affairs, while defenders aim to protect the system and maintain stability. Attackers may employ tactics like malicious code attacks and denial of service attacks, whereas defenders can utilize defensive strategies such as web services security strategy defense and code reconstruction defense. Achieving success in both aspects of the conflict is generally easier in the defensive realm, as defense strategies focus on repelling attacks, deterring through punishment, and assertive disarmament. The choice of offensive and defensive strategies depends on various factors, including the environment, the actions of the attacker, and the differing perceptions of the players.

Service and Reception Pattern

Getting the ball to somebody in a scoring position, such as a cross. This is also called service, generally. In gridiron football, a reception, also known informally as a catch, is part of a passing play in which a player in bounds successfully catches (receives) a forward pass thrown from a friendly quarterback behind the line of scrimmage.

Individual, Group and Team Tactics

Team tactics refer to the coordinated strategies, plans, and actions that a group of individuals employ to achieve specific goals or objectives. A group is a collection of individuals who coordinate their efforts, while a team is a group of people who share a common goal. While similar, the two are different when it comes to decision-making and teamwork. There are many tactics for attacking. When the opponent is playing perimeter defense, tip the ball to the middle of the court. If your setter plays across the front row, rather than setting one of the other two front row attackers, the setter could attack the 2nd ball. The best teams design plays. If you're opponent is slower at the net blocking, run a faster play. A quick set to the middle or shoot to the outside will make it difficult for the opponent to get in position to block.

Diet and nutrition for a Football Player

Nutritional needs vary based not only on the individual but also on the position they play. Nutrition plans must be individualized for each player based on their weight, height, body fat percentage, and position on the field. Nutrition is as important as training for footballers as it ensures that you can play to the best of your ability, while also recovering quickly post training or match. The best diet for a footballer is one which is high in calories as well as balanced in nutrients so your body is getting everything it needs. Due to the demands of the game and the physical expectations it puts on an individual, footballers must look after their bodies by considering what they consume before and after a game and training.

Coordination among the Manager, Coach, Doctor, Psychologist and Players

Coordination also allows for the more beneficial and efficient allocation of resources in an organization, which can reduce conflict and redundancies between individuals or departments. Coordination is the body's ability to perform smooth and efficient movements. Good coordination requires the athlete to combine multiple movements into a single movement that is fluid and achieves the intended goal. This is contrary to what many people first think of, which is hand-eye coordination which refers to the relationship between eye movements and hand movements, so that our hands make an intended movement in response to our eye movement, usually tracking a ball or something similar.

UNIT-III

Teaching of Football Skills

The fundamental skills of football give amateur and professional players the tools they need to compete and win.

- **Technique** – Ball control, Dribbling skills, Passing accuracy, Body control
- **Game intelligence** – Spatial awareness, Tactical knowledge, Risk assessment.
- **Physical fitness** – Endurance, Balance and coordination, Speed, Strength and power.
- **Proper mind-set** – Compassion, Composure and mental strength, Coach Ability, Self-motivation.

Preparing a Lesson Plan

Creating a lesson plan begins with aligning state standards to your curriculum and then narrowing the focus to determine which objectives you want your students to meet within a specific unit of study. Strong lesson plans are the foundation of an efficient classroom environment for both the teacher and the students. A lesson plan is the instructor's road map of what students need to learn and how it will be done effectively during the class time. Before you plan your lesson, you will first need to identify the learning objectives.

Specific Training Methods for Different Playing Positions

Position specific training drills are one of the most beneficial ways to improve a player's individual ability within a specific position. By continually placing players in scenarios specific to their position on the pitch, coaches can identify player's strengths and weaknesses, and then adjust their training drills accordingly to help develop and improve them. One of the main benefits of utilising position specific training drills within a training session is improving their positional sense. It's crucial that players are in the best position whether attacking or defending, both on and off the ball. They can also be used to develop a player's role in a position further, such as attacking higher, or defending deeper to help players become a better all-round player. Football is a dynamic sport that requires players to possess a wide range of physical abilities and tactical skills. Different positions within the game demand specific physical attributes, technical expertise, and strategic understanding. As a result, training methods vary depending on the position played in football.

Counselling During Competitions

A sport counsellor teaches an athlete to visualize successfully completing a certain action in sporting activity. This will give the athlete confidence to complete the maneuver as well as prepare the athletes body for the actual maneuver.

- Building and sustaining ideal level of motivation.
- Helping to achieve optimum level of self-Confidence.
- Enhancing Focus and concentration while dealing with distractions.
- Inculcating positivity and reducing negative self-talk.
- Managing competitive stress and anxiety.
- Building commitment towards one's sport and setting goals.
- Improving Team building and communication.
- Replacing fear of failure with desire to succeed.
- Managing and channelizing anger and negative emotions.
- Dealing with competitive pressure.
- Working on positive sport parenting.

Information and Publicity of the Competition

Publicity is a way of creating media attention on a service, product, or business by writing commercially important information on it in the media and not paying for time or space directly. Publicity adds credibility, has more data, is cost-effective, and is faster. Sports public relations is promoting teams, individual players and sports organizations through earned media channels including broadcast, print, radio, and online media outlets. Most colleges have many sports teams, and larger colleges may require multiple sports information directors to cover all of their teams. Typically, one sports information director may handle all information for all the sports for a college. This means that a sports information director should understand and appreciate most if not all sports. Since they work with sports in each season, it also means they work throughout the year but may have a break during the summer if they work at a college or high school.

Writing Press Release and Reports

A press release is an official statement (written or recorded) that an organization issues to the news media and beyond. A press release is a written communication distributed to members of the media with the primary purpose of announcing news, events, or information about a business, organization, or individual. A sports press release helps you share your story and let the world know what your sports event is all about, what makes it different and your visions as well. You can write a great press release by following a template or using a press release sample. The purpose of a sporting event press release is to inform the media, fans, and potential attendees about the event while generating anticipation and interest. A press release written for your sporting event can help you generate media attention giving you quick traction and brand trust as well.

Facility Management

Facilities management can be defined as the tools and services that support the functionality, safety, and sustainability of buildings, grounds, infrastructure, and real estate. Facilities managers help businesses optimize their workspaces to allow for function and safety while seeking opportunities to reduce costs. Working in facilities management can be a rewarding career with opportunities to advance to a manager or director position. Sport facilities can range from gyms and park and recreation departments to large arenas and stadiums. A Sport Facility Manager is responsible for managing and maintaining sport and recreation facilities. Sport facility management is the set of activities concerning the management and maintenance of sport facilities. Sports Facility Management involves a variety of tasks, such as budgeting, staffing, marketing, and customer service. It also includes the development and implementation of policies and procedures to ensure the safety and security of the facility and its patrons.

Quality Control of Equipment and Player's Kit

Quality control is a procedure or set of procedures intended to ensure that a manufactured product or performed service adheres to a defined set of quality criteria or meets the requirements of the client or customer. Quality control is essential for any company that manufactures products or provides a service. It helps improve customer satisfaction by consistently delivering quality products or services, reduce wastage of resources and increase efficiency and profits for the company.

Key components of Quality Control may include:

Testing
Conducting various tests and measurements to assess the performance, functionality, or characteristics of products or services.

Inspection
Regularly examining products, materials, or services to identify defects, non-compliance, or deviations from quality standards.

Statistical Process Control
Employing statistical techniques to monitor and control the production processes, ensuring that they remain within acceptable quality limits.

Corrective Action
Implementing appropriate measures to address any identified quality issues and prevent their recurrence.

Training and Education
Providing employees with the necessary skills and knowledge to maintain quality standards effectively.

Continuous Improvement
Constantly analyzing data and feedback to identify areas for improvement and enhancing the overall quality management system.

Documentation and Records
Keeping detailed records of inspections, tests, and corrective actions taken to maintain traceability and accountability.

Risk Management

Risk management is the process of identifying, assessing and controlling financial, legal, strategic and security risks to an organization's capital and earnings. Risk management is the set of steps an organization takes to prevent unwanted events from happening, or at least to reduce the damage of those events when they do happen. Effective risk management means attempting to control, as much as possible, future outcomes by acting proactively rather than reactively. Therefore, effective risk management offers the potential to reduce both the possibility of a risk occurring and its potential impact. Risk management is the systematic process of identifying, assessing, and mitigating threats or uncertainties that can affect your organization.

Medical Check-Up

Regular health check-ups can identify any early signs of health issues. Finding problems early means that your chances for effective treatment are increased. Many factors, such as your age, health, family history and lifestyle choices, impact on how often you need check-ups. A general medical check-up is a complete health evaluation by a physician or a nurse practitioner. It checks your overall health, determines if you have any health problems, and helps you understand what you can do to improve your health. A physical exam is an evaluation of your overall health. A primary care provider performs a physical exam. This exam focuses on preventive care so you can get to good health or maintain it. If your provider suspects a health concern or you have a concern, they may refer you to see a specialist or offer tests to learn more about your symptoms. You don't have to be ill to get a physical exam.

Medical Aid and Insurance

Medical aid covers members' healthcare costs such as hospitalisation, treatments and medicine. These costs are covered according to the rules of the medical scheme and the member's medical aid plan type. Health insurance provides several benefits. It offers financial protection by covering a significant portion of medical expenses. It ensures access to top-quality healthcare services at private facilities, including preventive care, screenings, check-ups, and treatments, which improve overall health, and early disease detection. Health insurance is an insurance product which covers medical and surgical expenses of an insured individual. It reimburses the expenses incurred due to illness or injury or pays the care provider of the insured individual directly.

Personnel Management

Personnel management is an administrative function within an organization that oversees the hiring, organization and support of employee positions. Personnel management deals with the managerial function of estimating and classifying human resources requirements for meeting organizational goals through people at work and their relationships with each other. A branch of human resources, personnel management focuses on recruiting the right individuals to fit a position and supporting those already working for the company. This area also functions as a tool for evaluating the hiring process and gaining insight into employee satisfaction. Personnel management is defined as an administrative specialization that focuses on hiring and developing employees to become more valuable to the company. It is sometimes considered to be a sub-category of human resources that only focuses on administration.

Interpersonal Communication Skills

Interpersonal communication is the process of exchange of information, ideas and feelings between two or more people through verbal or non-verbal methods. Face-to-face communication often involves hearing, seeing, and feeling body language, facial expressions, and gestures. In other terms, Interpersonal communication is exchanging information, meaning, feelings, and opinions between two or more people via verbal and non-verbal means. Interpersonal skills involve the ability to communicate and build relationships with others. Often called 'people skills', they tend to incorporate both your innate personality traits and how you have learned to handle certain social situations.

UNIT-IV

Injuries Associated With the Game:-

Ankle sprain

A sprained ankle is an injury that occurs when you roll, twist or turn your ankle in an awkward way. This can stretch or tear the tough bands of tissue (ligaments) that help hold your ankle bones together. An ankle sprain occurs when the strong ligaments that support the ankle stretch beyond their limits and tear. The severity of a sprain can vary greatly depending on the number of ligaments involved and the extent to which the ligaments are torn. A sprained ankle is when the ligaments in your ankle are torn. A broken ankle or ankle fracture is when one or more of the bones in your ankle break. Severe sprains and fractures have similar symptoms (pain, swelling, bruising, and tenderness) and are both caused by twisting or rotating your ankle, tripping or falling, or trauma to your ankle. Sprains heal faster, but it can take up to six weeks for a broken ankle to heal.

Finger injuries

Finger and hand injuries are common among athletes. Hand and finger injuries occur most often in contact sports, such as those that involve catching a ball or using hand equipment like ski poles or common sports, like basketball and volleyball. They also occur in high-speed sports like skating and biking. Finger injuries range from minor cuts and scrapes to wounds with significant damage to bone, tendons, and ligaments. If not treated properly, serious finger injuries can lead to permanent deformity and loss of function. Careful treatment allows for a faster and more complete recovery.

Shoulder dislocation

A dislocated shoulder is an injury in which the upper arm bone pops out of the cup-shaped socket that's part of the shoulder blade. The shoulder is the body's most flexible joint, which makes it more likely to dislocate. Dislocations happen when something pushes the bones in your shoulder joint out of their usual place. Shoulder dislocation can happen to anyone

and can be caused by trauma to the shoulder through sports injuries, falls or other accidents in which the shoulder is forced out of place. Shoulder dislocation can also occur as a result of overuse from repetitive activities or from previous dislocations that loosen connective tissues that keep the humerus in place within the socket.

Knee displacement

Kneecap dislocation occurs when the round-shaped bone covering the knee (patella) moves or slides out of place. The dislocation often occurs toward the outside of the leg. A dislocated knee is when the three bones of your knee are out of place and aren't aligned the way they should be. It can happen if the structures in your knee are abnormal. Some people are born with a knee dislocation (congenital dislocation of the knee). Most of the time, knee dislocations happen when a traumatic event thrusts the bones in your knee joint out of place with great force. It's an emergency, and it's very painful.

Preventive and Safety Measures

Stretching exercises

Stretching exercises can improve the ability of muscles to contract and perform, reducing the risk for injury. Each stretch should start slowly until you reach a point of muscle tension. Stretching should not be painful. Aim to hold each stretch for up to 20 seconds.

Wear the right gear

Players should wear appropriate and properly fit protective equipment such as pads (neck, shoulder, elbow, chest, knee, and shin), helmets, mouthpieces, face guards, protective cups, and eyewear. Young athletes should not assume that protective gear will prevent all injuries while performing more dangerous or risky activities.

Provide a healthy, well-balanced diet

It's important for athletes to eat a well-balanced diet full of fruits, vegetables and lean proteins, and to maintain a regular eating schedule. For instance, have breakfast, lunch and dinner around the same time each day. A poor diet that is high in processed foods and sugar can contribute to muscle weakness and decreased cardiovascular endurance. Hydration is equally important and should be maintained before, during, and after your workouts using water and electrolytes.

Cool Down

This is the most commonly forgotten portion of the workout. It helps safely bring the body, heart rate, and muscles back to their resting state. Perform 5-10 minutes of low-intensity cardiovascular activity, followed by stretching. Cooling down immediately after your workout will help decrease delayed onset muscle soreness and aid in recovery which will help prepare your body for its next workout.

Don't Play When You're Injured

This is a really important one. If you love sports, it's tempting to get right back in the game, even after an injury. But playing when you're hurt or before an injury has had a chance to fully heal is a bad idea. It can lead to an even worse injury, one that might side-line you for a long time.

Resume activity slowly

Don't be tempted to nurse your injury for too long. Excessive rest may delay healing. After the initial 48-hour period of RICE, you can start using heat to help relax tight muscles. Take things slowly, and ease back in to exercise or your sport of choice.

Maintain flexibility

It is extremely important that you do dynamic stretches before starting your activity. Cold muscles are more prone to injury, so, while it may be tempting to start playing immediately, you should take a few minutes to do some jumping jacks, butt kicks, or arm circles first.

P.R.I.C.E.

Protection, Rest, Ice, Compression and Elevation, or P.R.I.C.E., adds the concept of "protection" to the traditional R.I.C.E. protocol formula.

Protecting the injured area from further damage is crucial to the healing process. Protect the injured person and the area being treated but also protect yourself. If the injury occurs on the sports field, stop the game.

Rehabilitation and Physiotherapy

Rehabilitation is care that can help you get back, keep, or improve abilities that you need for daily life. Physiotherapy helps through physical rehabilitation, injury prevention, and health and fitness. Physiotherapists get you involved in your own recovery. The terms "physiotherapy" and "physical therapy" mean the same thing and are used interchangeably, as are the terms “physiotherapist” and “physical therapist”. Physiotherapists have in-depth knowledge of how the body works and specialized hands-on clinical skills to assess, diagnose, and treat symptoms of illness, injury and disability. Physiotherapy is treatment to restore, maintain, and make the most of a patient’s mobility, function, and well-being. Physiotherapists work with clients of all ages and with a wide range of health conditions. Whether its pain management and rehabilitation from an acute injury like a sprained ankle or management of chronic conditions such as diabetes or heart disease, a physiotherapist can help. Physical therapy is provided by physical therapists who promote, maintain or restore the wellbeing through examination, diagnosis, prognosis, patient education, physiotherapeutic intervention, rehabilitation, disease prevention and health promotion.

Training Means for Development of Different Components of Physical Fitness

Speed

Speed in physical education is one of the most important fitness components, whether one plays sports or not, everyone wants speed because actions in everyday life situations need to be carried out at the appropriate speed to be able to achieve success. Speed has a direct relationship with the nervous system and the muscular system. Speed in physical education is considered a physical component. The brain and nervous system control and coordinate the movements of our muscles. Speed is defined as the ability to move the body in one direction as fast as possible. Speed is one of the main fitness components, important for success in many sports. Speed is important in sprinting, speed skating, sprint cycling and sports such as tennis when a player has to move forward quickly from the baseline to reach a drop shot close to the net.

Strength

Strength is one of the main fitness components, important for success in many sports. Certain sports, such as weight lifting, wrestling and weight throwing, it is the most important physical attribute. A strength exercise is any activity that makes your muscles work harder than usual. This increases your muscles' strength, size, power and endurance. The activities involve using your body weight or working against a resistance. Strength is the ability of a muscle to exert force in single muscle contraction or it is the ability to overcome resistance. Strength is an essential component of physical fitness. Strength refers to the quality or state of being strong. Our muscles are vital to our bodies and are the reasons we can walk, run, carry things, and so much more. But muscles start to deteriorate as we age, so finding ways such as resistance training to build muscle is crucial.

Endurance

Endurance is defined as the ability to continue despite fatigue or difficult conditions. The stamina to perform physical activities for longer periods of time can be improved by exercise and increasing the amount of activity. Endurance refers to an individual's ability to sustain physical activity or mental effort over an extended period. It is the capacity to withstand fatigue, stress, and discomfort while maintaining optimal performance levels. Endurance is a crucial aspect of athletic performance and overall fitness, enabling athletes to compete and excel in various sports. Endurance is the capacity of a person to work in unpleasant and hard situation without giving up. In physical education, endurance is explained as the capacity to work against fatigue. Endurance refers to your body's physical capability to sustain an exercise for an extended period. It's made up of two components: cardiovascular endurance and muscular endurance. Cardiovascular endurance is the ability of your heart and lungs to fuel your body with oxygen. Muscular endurance is the ability of your muscles to work continuously without getting tired.

Flexibility

Flexibility is an important part of physical fitness and is defined as the ability to move the joints freely. Both range of motion and mobility are common terms when discussing flexibility. Range of motion is how much a joint or body part can move and mobility is how easy it is to move. Flexibility can be assessed using various methods depending on the specific joints or muscle groups being evaluated. Flexibility helps performance, posture, promotes efficient movement, prevents incorrect body alignment, maintains appropriate muscle length and balance and also decreases injury risk. Flexibility is the ability to move muscles and joints through a full normal range of motion. Flexibility refers to the ability of muscles, joints, and soft tissues to move through an unrestricted, pain-free range of motion. It involves the capacity of these structures to stretch, lengthen, and contract without limitations, allowing for smooth and efficient movement.

Co-coordinative Abilities

Coordination is understood, in general terms, as the ability of the human body to unify in a synchronised manner the work of various muscles in the execution of an intentional action. Gross motor coordination involves the large muscles in your arms, legs, and torso, which you use for everyday activities like walking, lifting, throwing, running, and kicking. Fine motor coordination focuses on coordination of the small muscles in your hands and wrists the ones you use to write, type on your computer or phone, or do activities like sewing. Hand/eye coordination is the coordination of the information your eyes take in, and the signals your brain sends to your arms and hands. You rely on this to do everyday tasks like drive a car, cook, or pick up something. Coordination is the ability to select the right muscle at the right time with proper intensity to achieve proper action. Coordinated movement is characterized by appropriate speed, distance, direction, timing and muscular tension. Coordination is about our motor skills and can be broken up into fine or gross motor skills. Fine motor skills are about our coordination in relation to small movements and the ease they are performed. An example of a fine motor skill in sport is the snooker shot. Conversely, gross motor skills involve large movements and muscle groups. Examples of gross motor skills include walking, kicking, jumping and much more.

Practical Course

Course Code: PED303PR

Specialization in Kabaddi

UNIT-I

History of Game

Kabaddi is basically a combative sport, with seven players on each side; played for a period of 40 minutes with a 5 minutes break (20-5-20). The core idea of the game is to score points by raiding into the opponent's court and touching as many defense players as possible without getting caught on a single breath.

The overall object of the game is to simply score more points than the opposition team within the allotted time. To do this, each team must attempt to score points by both attacking and defending. When attacking, the offensive team sends across a raider into the opposition's half who must touch one of more members of the opposition to score a point. The evolution of Kabaddi can be traced back to India. The International governing body for Kabaddi is the International Kabaddi Federation (IKB), formed in 2004. In 1972, the sport became the national game of Bangladesh and in 1978, after the Asian Amateur Kabaddi Federation was established, a regional championship was organized. National kabaddi teams began to compete in the Asian Games in 1990 and in 2004, the first Kabaddi World Cup took place in Mumbai. It hosted national teams from across the world, such as Asia, Europe and North America.

Measurement and preparation of the play field

Kabaddi mat dimensions may vary according to tournaments and age groups, but it mostly measures 13m x 10m for senior men's professional kabaddi events. The mat is slightly smaller, 12m x 8m, for women. The objective of a single player in offence, known as a raider is to touch the maximum number of defenders from the opposite team and come back to their part of the court.

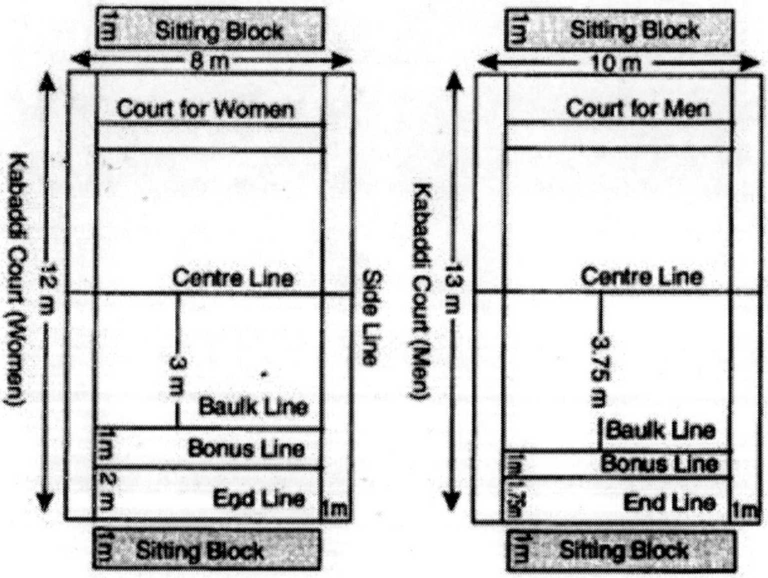

Equipment Required For Game

Knee Caps and Elbow Guards
You can either buy a pre-made kabaddi kit that includes all the necessary equipment, or you can purchase each item separately. Knee caps and elbow guards are not compulsory in kabaddi but are recommended, especially for children. They protect the joints from knocks and scrapes.

Kabaddi Shoes

Kabaddi shoes are designed to provide good grip and traction, so players can move quickly and change directions easily. They also have thick soles to protect the feet from getting stepped on. The right pair of shoes can make all the difference in a kabaddi match.

Kabaddi Mat

This line is important because it is where the two teams start the game from. The kabaddi mat is usually made out of cloth or rubber. It is important to make sure that the mat you use is thick enough so that you do not hurt yourself when you fall on it. The kabaddi mat also has a line in the middle of it which is called the mid-line.

Fundamental Skills and Lead-Up Games

Offensive skills in kabaddi

Hand Touch

After entering the opposition half or crossing the midline, a raider performs a hand touch by extending his arm to touch the defender. Hand touch is one of the most common scoring skills for a raider. Running hand touch is an advanced version of the regular move which requires raiders to touch defenders while being on the move during a raid. It requires an optimal level of agility and flexibility for a raider to successfully execute this move.

Toe Touch

A toe touch takes place when a raider swiftly bends down and scores points by using his foot to make contact with a defender. Heavily reliant on speed and catching defenders off guard, the toe touch is a spontaneous move attempted by a raider to outfox unassuming defenders. The move, if mastered, is also effective to score bonus points when six or more defenders are on the mat.

Back Kick

Back kick in kabaddi is one of the cleverest skills in which the raider deceives the defence by showing his back and tries to kick backwards to receive a touch point. It is also called a 'mule kick' in some parts of the world.

Dubki

A move that requires exceptional timing and sharp instincts to be pulled off is a Dubki. In a dubki, the raider evades the chain tackle while ducking below the stretched arms of the defenders and scoring a point.

Lion Jump

Popularised by Pawan Sehrawat in Vivo Pro Kabaddi, Lion Jump requires unbelievable power and thrust generated from the legs of the raider. A kabaddi raider tries to jump over the defenders to escape and reach the midline in a lion jump. This move is widely considered as the most athletic move in the game and is incredibly difficult to perform, let alone master.

Defensive skills

Ankle hold

This is a counter skill used by defensive players against leg thrusts and foot touches during an attack or raid. A team, which has mastery over ankle hold, can plan different strategies and tactics in various situations, such as, (a) lifting up (b) pulling back (c) changing direction of the raider.

Thigh hold

This skill is a good defensive skill. Every team uses this technique as a planned and surprise tactic. For example: (a) Taking one step forward and hold Taking one step forward means holding the raider's thigh on wrong step or rear leg (b) thigh hold from behind.

Waist hold or trunk hold

Waist hold is a skill used by a defender to catch the raider from behind.

Wrist hold

Wrist hold is also a defensive skill and used occasionally only when a situation presents itself. This hold is rarely used now a days.

Blocking

It is a defensive skill used by covers and corners. Blocking is an act of creating a wall of obstruction in the path of the raider to prevent the movement. The aim of blocking is not just to obstruct the path, but also to catch the raider.

Techniques, Strategies and Method of Play

1 Running.
2 Dodging & Stooping.
3 Skipping & Side/Back Stepping.
4 Balancing (Dynamic Balance & Static Balance)
5 Kicking (Back, Front & Side Kick)

Rules and Regulations of the Game

1. To win a point when raiding, the raider must take a breath and run into the opposition's half and tag one or more members of the opposing team and then return to their own half of the pitch before inhaling again.
2. As per kabaddi rules, a match starts with one team raiding the other team's half.
3. The objective of the raider is to tag or touch as many opposition players, called antis or defenders, as possible and return to their own half by crossing the mid line while continuing their cant under one breath.
4. During a raid, any one player from the attacking team, called the raider, enters the other team's half while chanting the word kabaddi, also known as canting.
5. There are six officials looking after each Kabaddi match. The officials comprise of a referee, a scorer, two assistant scorers and two umpires.
6. The duration of the match is two halves of 20 minutes with a half time break of 5 minutes.
7. However, in case of a knockout match if the game ends in a tie, an extra seven minutes will be added to decide the outcome of the contest. The seven minutes are divided into two halves of three minutes each with a one minute break in between the two.
8. At the start of a Kabaddi match, there is a coin toss with the winner having the choice as to whether to have the first raid or not. In the second half of the match, the team that did not raid first shall begin the second half with a raid.

National and International Tournaments Associated with the Game

- Pro Kabaddi League
- National Kabaddi Championship
- Federation Cup
- Beach National Kabaddi Championship
- Departmental National Kabaddi Championship
- Pandit Deen Dayal Upadhyay Memorial All India National Style Kabaddi Championship
- Telangana Premier kabaddi Leauge

Team/Individual records (World, Olympic, Asian and National Level) of the Game

World Championships

Kabaddi World Cup Winners List

Year	Host	Winner	Runner-Up	Score
2004	Mumbai	India	Iran	55-27
2007	Panvel	India	Iran	29-19
2010	Ludhiana	India	Pakistan	58-24
2011	Ludhiana	India	Canada	59-25
2012	Ludhiana	India	Pakistan	59-22
2013	Ludhiana	India	Pakistan	48-39
2014	Sri Mukhtar Sahib	India	Pakistan	45-42
2016	Ahmadabad	India	Iran	38-29
2020	Pakistan	Pakistan	India	41-39

Asian Games

Asian Games kabaddi medal winners list - men's

Edition	Gold Medal	Silver Medal	Bronze Medal
1990	India	Bangladesh	Pakistan

1994	India	Bangladesh	Pakistan
1998	India	Pakistan	Bangladesh
2002	India	Bangladesh	Pakistan
2006	India	Pakistan	Bangladesh
2010	India	Iran	Pakistan, Japan
2014	India	Iran	South Korea, Pakistan
2018	Iran	South Korea	Pakistan, India
2023	India	Iran	Pakistan, Chinese Taipei

Asian Games kabaddi medal winners list - women's

Edition	Gold Medal	Silver Medal	Bronze Medal
2010	India	Thailand	Bangladesh, Iran
2014	India	Iran	Thailand, Bangladesh
2018	Iran	India	Chinese Taipei, Thailand
2023	India	Chinese Taipei	Nepal, Iran

National Level

Padma Shri

Year of Award	Name of Recipient	State
2014	Ms. Sunil Dabas	Haryana
2019	Mr. Ajay Thakur	Himachal Pradesh

Dhyanchand Award Winners of Kabaddi

Year of Award	Name of Recipient	State
2007	Mr. Shamsher Singh	Haryana
2020	Mr. Manpreet Singh	ONGC
2021	Mr. Vikas Kumar	Haryana
2022	BC Suresh	

Dronacharya Award Winners of Kabaddi

Year	Name of Recipient	State
2002	Mr. Ejjapureddi Prasad Rao	Andhra Pradesh
2005	Mr. Balwan Singh	Services
2012	Ms. Sunil Dabas	Haryana
2019	Mr. Rambir Singh Khokhar (Life Time)	Haryana
2020	Mr. Krishan Kumar Hooda (Life Time)	Haryana
2021	Mr. Ashan Kumar (Life Time)	Haryana

Arjun Award Winners of Kabaddi

Year	Name of Recipient	State
1972	Mr. Sahanand Mahadev Shetty	Maharashtra
1973	Mr. Bholanath Guin	West Bengal
1978	Ms. Shakuntala Pandarinath Khatavkar	Maharashtra
1980	Mr. Shantaram Jadhav	Maharashtra
1981	Ms. Monika Nath	West Bengal
1983	Ms. Maya Kashinath	Maharashtra
1986	Ms. Rama Sarkar	West Bengal
1990	Mr. Hardeep Singh	SSCB
1994	Mr. S. Rajarathnam	Tamil Nadu
1994	Mr. Ashok Shinde	Maharashtra
1995	Mr. P. Ganeshan	Tamil Nadu
1996	Mr. Shriram Bhavsar	Maharashtra
1996	Ms. Neeta Moreshwer Dadwe	Indian Railway
1997	Mr. Randhir Singh	Delhi
1998	Mr. Ashan Kumar	SSCB
1998	Mr. Bishwajit Palit	West Bengal
1999	Mr. Balwinder Singh (Piddha)	Punjab
1999	Mr. Tirath Raj	Delhi
2000	Mr. C. Honnappa Gowda	Karnataka

2001	Mr. B.C. Ramesh	Karnataka
2002	Mr. Ram Mehar Singh	SSCB
2003	Mr. Sanjeev Kumar	Indian Railway
2004	Mr. Sunder Singh	Delhi
2005	Mr. Ramesh Kumar	Haryana
2006	Mr. Navneet Gautam	Rajasthan
2009	Mr. Pankaj Navnath Shirsat	Maharashtra
2010	Mr. Dinesh Kumar	Delhi
2011	Mr. Rakesh Kumar	Indian Railway
2011	Ms. Tejeswini Bai V	Indian Railway
2012	Mr. Anoop Kumar	Delhi
2013	NONE	
2014	Ms. Mamtha Poojari	Indian Railway
2015	Mr. Manjeet Chhillar	Indian Railway
2015	Ms. Abhilasha Shashikant Mahatre	Indian Railway
2016	NONE	
2017	Mr. Jasvir Singh	ONGC
2018	NONE	
2019	Mr. Ajay Thakur	Himachal Pradesh
2020	Mr. Deepak Hooda	Rajasthan
2021	Mr. Sandeep Narwal	Haryana
2022	Sakshi Kumari	Haryana

Awards Associated With the Game

- Arjuna Award
- Dhyan Chand Award
- Dronacharya Award
- Ekalavya Award

Duties of the Officials

Referee – He has the power to warn, declare point against or disqualify a participant from match. He has the authority to overturn the decision given by umpire.

Umpire – generally the decision of the umpire taken as final.
Scorer – the scorer fills the scores data, timings, time-outs.
Assistant Scorers – they record those players who are out and those who are survived.

Technical Equipment for Officiating

- Game clock and stop watch.
- 30 second devices
- Score sheet
- Whistles
- Score board
- Player foul marker
- Team foul marker.

Knowledge of the Score Sheets

Points are scored for each player tagged by the raider, while the opposing team earns a point for stopping the raider.

Date: .... Time: .... Place: .... Ground No: ....

Toss won by: .... Team, Choose: **Raid/ Court**

Team:									**Vs**	**Team:**								
1st Seven Players										1st Seven Players								
Reserved Player										Reserved Player								
Time out		I Half		Official	II Half		Official			Time out		I Half		Official	II Half		Official	
		1	2		1	2						1	2		1	2		
Substitution	IN									Substitution	IN							
	OUT										OUT							
Team Warning										Team Warning								
TIE BREAKER										**TIE BREAKER**								
Order of 5 raids							**Total**			**Order of 5 raids**							**Total**	
Points Details	Scored									**Points Details**	Scored							
	Lost										Lost							

S.No.	**Name of the Players**	**Chest No.**	**S.No.**	**Name of the Players**	**Chest No.**
1.			1.		
2.			2.		
3.			3.		
4.			4.		
5.			5.		
6.			6.		
7.			7.		
8.			8.		
9.			9.		
10.			10.		
11.			11.		
12.			12.		
Coach :			**Coach** :		
Manager :			**Manager** :		

RUNNING SCORE											(Keys: Out /	Bonus Δ,		Lona --		Technical O,			First Leading □)				
1	2	3	4	5	6	7	8	9	10	11	12	1	2	3	4	5	6	7	8	9	10	11	12
13	14	15	16	17	18	19	20	21	22	23	24	13	14	15	16	17	18	19	20	21	22	23	24
25	26	27	28	29	30	31	32	33	34	35	36	25	26	27	28	29	30	31	32	33	34	35	36
37	38	39	40	41	42	43	44	45	46	47	48	37	38	39	40	41	42	43	44	45	46	47	48
49	50	51	52	53	54	55	56	57	58	58	60	49	50	51	52	53	54	55	56	57	58	58	60
61	62	63	64	65	66	67	68	69	70	71	72	61	62	63	64	65	66	67	68	69	70	71	72

POINTS DETAILS

Particulars	OUT	BONUS	LONA	TECH	TOTAL	Particulars	OUT	BONUS	LONA	TECH	TOTAL
1st HALF						1st HALF					
2nd HALF						2nd HALF					
5 Raids						5 Raids					
Golden Raid						Golden Raid					
Total						**Total**					

RESULT: This match won by____________________ team with ________ points

Signature's for Officials

Scorer: Umpire - 1: Umpire - 2: Referee:

Players are taken out of the game if they are touched or tackled, but are brought back in for each point scored by their team from a tag or a tackle.

Signals of Officiating

UNIT-II

General Warming-Up

The general warm-up should consist of a light physical activity, like walking, jogging, easy swimming, stationary bike riding, skipping or easy aerobics. Both the intensity and duration of the general warm-up (or how hard and how long), should be governed by the fitness level of the participating athlete. To begin your warm-up do 5 minutes of light (low intensity) physical activity such as walking, jogging on the spot or on a trampoline, or cycling. Pump your arms or make large but controlled circular movements with your arms to help warm the muscles of your upper body.

Specific Warming-Up

In this type of warm-up specific types of exercises are performed after the activities of general warm-up. Specific type of warming-up differs from activity to activity. A specific warm-up is when you focus on just the areas of your body you are working on that day. So if you are working on increasing your speed on the track one day, you design your specific warm-up to support that goal.

Cooling Down

A cool down is designed to promote recovery and return the body to a pre-exercise or pre-workout level. This can be accomplished in a variety of different ways. You can walk or jog, stretch, or even engage in mindfulness to help your body relax and recover. Whether physical or mental activities or a combination of both a cool down helps you recover mentally and physically after physical activity or exercise. Cooling down after your workout lets the heart rate and blood pressure slowly recover to preexercise levels. It may be most important for competitive endurance athletes, such as marathoners, to cool down to help control blood flow. Cooling down doesn't seem to help reduce muscle stiffness and soreness after exercise, but more research is needed. A cool down eases you out of your workout and allows your heart rate and breathing to gradually return to normal.

Long-Term and Short-Term Preparation for the Decisive Kabaddi Competitions

Being fit in Kabaddi means having the stamina to keep going, the strength to tackle opponents, and the agility to dodge them. Your fitness level directly impacts your ability to contribute to your team's success. Work on your cardio, strength training, and flexibility to improve your performance on the kabaddi court. Learn different tagging techniques such as ankle hold, waist hold, and thigh hold. Practice these techniques to become more effective at tagging opponents. Engage in exercises like running, cycling, or skipping to build stamina. Kabaddi is a high-intensity sport, and good cardiovascular health is essential.

Psychological Qualities and Preparation of a Kabaddi Player

For being a kabaddi player both fitness and smartness is required. There are several positions in kabaddi such as defender, raider. If the player best in raiding he should also know to defend and some tackling strategies because his raiding points helps team to score. Kabaddi players, on the basis of their role in the game, can be divided into four groups, namely Raiders, Corners, Coverers and All-rounders. The raiders are attackers; corners and coverers are defenders, whereas all-rounders perform both duties of attacking and defending. The main responsibility of the corners is to initiate the tackles at the right moment, as they are the main targets for the opposition's raiders to score points from.

Offensive, Defense System in Play

Offensive and defensive strategies in defense refer to the actions taken by individuals involved in a game or conflict situation. The goal of attackers is to disrupt the current state of affairs, while defenders aim to protect the system and maintain stability. Attackers may employ tactics like malicious code attacks and denial of service attacks, whereas defenders can utilize defensive strategies such as web services security strategy defense and code reconstruction defense. Achieving success in both aspects of the conflict is generally easier in the defensive realm, as defense strategies focus on repelling attacks, deterring through punishment, and assertive disarmament. The choice of offensive and defensive strategies depends on various factors, including the environment, the actions of the attacker, and the differing perceptions of the players.

Service and Reception Pattern

A kabaddi match typically runs for 40 minutes (two halves of 20 minutes each). The match starts with a coin toss between the two teams and the winner can decide whether to raid or defend first. Each team is allowed two time-outs in each half. As per kabaddi rules, a match starts with one team raiding the other team's half. During a raid, any one player from the attacking team, called the raider, enters the other team's half while chanting the word kabaddi, also known as canting. The objective of the raider is to tag or touch as many opposition players, called antis or defenders, as possible and return to their own half by crossing the mid line while continuing their cant under one breath. The defenders, meanwhile, try to stop the raider from returning to his own half by tackling or pushing him out of the court.

Individual, Group and Team Tactics

Team tactics refer to the coordinated strategies, plans, and actions that a group of individuals employ to achieve specific goals or objectives. A group is a collection of individuals who coordinate their efforts, while a team is a group of people who share a common goal. While similar, the two are different when it comes to decision-making and teamwork. There are many tactics for attacking. When the opponent is playing perimeter defense, tip the ball to the middle of the court. If your setter plays across the front row, rather than setting one of the other two front row attackers, the setter could attack the 2nd ball. The best teams design plays. If you're opponent is slower at the net blocking, run a faster play. A quick set to the middle or shoot to the outside will make it difficult for the opponent to get in position to block.

Diet and Nutrition for a Kabaddi Player

A kabaddi player needs to eat for about 5 times a day and typically is a high calorie diet, because Kabaddi as a sport requires extremely strong muscles and physical strength and only high intensity training can produce that kind of muscle and strength. And for such training, they need a high calorie diet.

Kabaddi or the game of the masses as it is rightly called is an extremely physically demanding sport. It involves a great deal of muscular co-ordination, agility, quick responses, decision-making skills, presence of mind and breath-holding capacity.

Coordination among the manager, coach, doctor, psychologist and players

Coordination also allows for the more beneficial and efficient allocation of resources in an organization, which can reduce conflict and redundancies between individuals or departments. Coordination is the body's ability to perform smooth and efficient movements. Good coordination requires the athlete to combine multiple movements into a single movement that is fluid and achieves the intended goal. This is contrary to what many people first think of, which is hand-eye coordination which refers to the relationship between eye movements and hand movements, so that our hands make an intended movement in response to our eye movement, usually tracking a ball or something similar.

UNIT-III

Teaching of kabaddi skills

There are broadly two categories of skills that a kabaddi player needs to learn are offensive skills and defensive skills. For example, during a raid, a raider must try to touch the antis with the maximum use of his limbs. It will make easy for him and for his team to score points.

Preparing a lesson plan

Creating a lesson plan begins with aligning state standards to your curriculum and then narrowing the focus to determine which objectives you want your students to meet within a specific unit of study. Strong lesson plans are the foundation of an efficient classroom environment for both the teacher and the students. A lesson plan is the instructor's road map of what students need to learn and how it will be done effectively during the class time. Before you plan your lesson, you will first need to identify the learning objectives.

Specific training methods for different playing positions

Develop your muscles, especially in the upper and lower body, through strength training. Exercises like squats, push-ups, and weightlifting can enhance your physical power. Incorporate agility drills into your training routine. These drills involve quick movements and directional changes, helping you become more agile on the field. Regular stretching or yoga sessions can improve your flexibility, making you more agile and resilient during the game. Sit-ups and crunches are traditional workout routines that most people already know about. What makes it important to Kabaddi is the fact that the core or abdomen is one of the most important parts of the body in the sport. Applying this workout to your routine helps you increase your capacity to endure opponents' push against you and defend your position.

Counselling During Competitions

A sport counsellor teaches an athlete to visualize successfully completing a certain action in sporting activity. This will give the athlete confidence to complete the maneuver as well as prepare the athletes body for the actual maneuver.

- Building and sustaining ideal level of motivation.
- Helping to achieve optimum level of self-Confidence.
- Enhancing Focus and concentration while dealing with distractions.
- Inculcating positivity and reducing negative self-talk.
- Managing competitive stress and anxiety.
- Building commitment towards one's sport and setting goals.
- Improving Team building and communication.
- Replacing fear of failure with desire to succeed.
- Managing and channelizing anger and negative emotions.
- Dealing with competitive pressure.
- Working on positive sport parenting.

Information and Publicity of the Competition

Publicity is a way of creating media attention on a service, product, or business by writing commercially important information on it in the media and not paying for time or space directly. Publicity adds credibility, has more data, is cost-effective, and is faster. Sports public relations is promoting teams, individual players and sports organizations through earned media channels including broadcast, print, radio, and online media outlets. Most colleges have many sports teams, and larger colleges may require multiple sports information directors to cover all of their teams. Typically, one sports information director may handle all information for all the sports for a college. This means that a sports information director should understand and appreciate most if not all sports. Since they work with sports in each season, it also means they work throughout the year but may have a break during the summer if they work at a college or high school.

Writing Press Release and Reports

A press release is an official statement (written or recorded) that an organization issues to the news media and beyond. A press release is a written communication distributed to members of the media with the primary purpose of announcing news, events, or information about a business, organization, or individual. A sports press release helps you share your story and let the world know what your sports event is all about, what makes it different and your visions as well. You can write a great press release by following a template or using a press release sample. The purpose of a sporting event press release is to inform the media, fans, and potential attendees about the event while generating anticipation and interest. A press release written for your sporting event can help you generate media attention giving you quick traction and brand trust as well.

Facility Management

Facilities management can be defined as the tools and services that support the functionality, safety, and sustainability of buildings, grounds, infrastructure, and real estate. Facilities managers help businesses optimize their workspaces to allow for function and safety while seeking opportunities to reduce costs. Working in facilities management can be a rewarding career with opportunities to advance to a manager or director position. Sport facilities can range from gyms and park and recreation departments to large arenas and stadiums. A Sport Facility Manager is responsible for managing and maintaining sport and recreation facilities. Sport facility management is the set of activities concerning the management and maintenance of sport facilities. Sports Facility Management involves a variety of tasks, such as budgeting, staffing, marketing, and customer service. It also includes the development and implementation of policies and procedures to ensure the safety and security of the facility and its patrons.

Quality Control of Equipment and Player's Kit

Quality control is a procedure or set of procedures intended to ensure that a manufactured product or performed service adheres to a defined set of quality criteria or meets the requirements of the client or customer. Quality control is essential for any company that manufactures products or provides a service. It helps improve customer satisfaction by consistently delivering quality products or services, reduce wastage of resources and increase efficiency and profits for the company.

Key components of Quality Control may include:

Testing
Conducting various tests and measurements to assess the performance, functionality, or characteristics of products or services.
Inspection
Regularly examining products, materials, or services to identify defects, non-compliance, or deviations from quality standards.

Statistical Process Control
Employing statistical techniques to monitor and control the production processes, ensuring that they remain within acceptable quality limits.

Corrective Action
Implementing appropriate measures to address any identified quality issues and prevent their recurrence.
Training and Education
Providing employees with the necessary skills and knowledge to maintain quality standards effectively.

Continuous Improvement
Constantly analyzing data and feedback to identify areas for improvement and enhancing the overall quality management system.

Documentation and Records
Keeping detailed records of inspections, tests, and corrective actions taken to maintain traceability and accountability.

Risk Management

Risk management is the process of identifying, assessing and controlling financial, legal, strategic and security risks to an organization's capital and earnings. Risk management is the set of steps an organization takes to prevent unwanted events from happening, or at least to reduce the damage of those events when they do happen. Effective risk management means attempting to control, as much as possible, future outcomes by acting proactively rather than reactively. Therefore, effective risk management offers the potential to reduce both the possibility of a risk occurring and its potential impact. Risk management is the systematic process of identifying, assessing, and mitigating threats or uncertainties that can affect your organization.

Medical Check-Up

Regular health check-ups can identify any early signs of health issues. Finding problems early means that your chances for effective treatment are increased. Many factors, such as your age, health, family history and lifestyle choices, impact on how often you need check-ups. A general medical check-up is a complete health evaluation by a physician or a nurse practitioner. It checks your overall health, determines if you have any health problems, and helps you understand what you can do to improve your health. A physical exam is an evaluation of your overall health. A primary care provider performs a physical exam. This exam focuses on preventive care so you can get to good health or maintain it. If your provider suspects a health concern or you have a concern, they may refer you to see a specialist or offer tests to learn more about your symptoms. You don't have to be ill to get a physical exam.

Medical Aid and Insurance

Medical aid covers members' healthcare costs such as hospitalisation, treatments and medicine. These costs are covered according to the rules of the medical scheme and the member's medical aid plan type. Health insurance provides several benefits. It offers financial protection by covering a significant portion of medical expenses. It ensures access to top-quality healthcare services at private facilities, including preventive care, screenings, check-ups, and treatments, which improve overall health, and early disease detection. Health insurance is an insurance product which covers medical and surgical expenses of an insured individual. It reimburses the expenses incurred due to illness or injury or pays the care provider of the insured individual directly.

Personnel Management

Personnel management is an administrative function within an organization that oversees the hiring, organization and support of employee positions. Personnel management deals with the managerial function of estimating and classifying human resources requirements for meeting organizational goals through people at work and their relationships with each other. A branch of human resources, personnel management focuses on recruiting the right individuals to fit a position and supporting those already working for the company. This area also functions as a tool for evaluating the hiring process and gaining insight into employee satisfaction. Personnel management is defined as an administrative specialization that focuses on hiring and developing employees to become more valuable to the company. It is sometimes considered to be a sub-category of human resources that only focuses on administration.

Interpersonal Communication Skills

Interpersonal communication is the process of exchange of information, ideas and feelings between two or more people through verbal or non-verbal methods. Face-to-face communication often involves hearing, seeing, and feeling body language, facial expressions, and gestures. In other terms, Interpersonal communication is exchanging information, meaning, feelings, and opinions between two or more people via verbal and non-verbal means. Interpersonal skills involve the ability to communicate and build relationships with others. Often called 'people skills', they tend to incorporate both your innate personality traits and how you have learned to handle certain social situations.

UNIT-IV

Injuries Associated With the Game:-

Ankle sprain

A sprained ankle is an injury that occurs when you roll, twist or turn your ankle in an awkward way. This can stretch or tear the tough bands of tissue (ligaments) that help hold your ankle bones together. An ankle sprain occurs when the strong ligaments that support the ankle stretch beyond their limits and tear. The severity of a sprain can vary greatly depending on the number of ligaments involved and the extent to which the ligaments are torn. A sprained ankle is when the ligaments in your ankle are torn. A broken ankle or ankle fracture is when one or more of the bones in your ankle break. Severe sprains and fractures have similar symptoms (pain, swelling, bruising, and tenderness) and are both caused by twisting or rotating your ankle, tripping or falling, or trauma to your ankle. Sprains heal faster, but it can take up to six weeks for a broken ankle to heal.

Finger injuries

Finger and hand injuries are common among athletes. Hand and finger injuries occur most often in contact sports, such as those that involve catching a ball or using hand equipment like ski poles or common sports, like basketball and volleyball. They also occur in high-speed sports like skating and biking. Finger injuries range from minor cuts and scrapes to wounds with significant damage to bone, tendons, and ligaments. If not treated properly, serious finger injuries can lead to permanent deformity and loss of function. Careful treatment allows for a faster and more complete recovery.

Shoulder Dislocation

A dislocated shoulder is an injury in which the upper arm bone pops out of the cup-shaped socket that's part of the shoulder blade. The shoulder is the body's most flexible joint, which makes it more likely to dislocate. Dislocations happen when something pushes the bones in your shoulder joint out of their usual place. Shoulder dislocation can happen to anyone

and can be caused by trauma to the shoulder through sports injuries, falls or other accidents in which the shoulder is forced out of place. Shoulder dislocation can also occur as a result of overuse from repetitive activities or from previous dislocations that loosen connective tissues that keep the humerus in place within the socket.

Knee displacement

Kneecap dislocation occurs when the round-shaped bone covering the knee (patella) moves or slides out of place. The dislocation often occurs toward the outside of the leg. A dislocated knee is when the three bones of your knee are out of place and aren't aligned the way they should be. It can happen if the structures in your knee are abnormal. Some people are born with a knee dislocation (congenital dislocation of the knee). Most of the time, knee dislocations happen when a traumatic event thrusts the bones in your knee joint out of place with great force. It's an emergency, and it's very painful.

Preventive and Safety Measures

Stretching exercises

Stretching exercises can improve the ability of muscles to contract and perform, reducing the risk for injury. Each stretch should start slowly until you reach a point of muscle tension. Stretching should not be painful. Aim to hold each stretch for up to 20 seconds.

Wear the right gear

Players should wear appropriate and properly fit protective equipment such as pads (neck, shoulder, elbow, chest, knee, and shin), helmets, mouthpieces, face guards, protective cups, and eyewear. Young athletes should not assume that protective gear will prevent all injuries while performing more dangerous or risky activities.

Provide a healthy, well-balanced diet

It's important for athletes to eat a well-balanced diet full of fruits, vegetables and lean proteins, and to maintain a regular eating schedule. For instance, have breakfast, lunch and dinner around the same time each day. A poor diet that is high in processed foods and sugar can contribute to muscle weakness and decreased cardiovascular endurance. Hydration is equally important and should be maintained before, during, and after your workouts using water and electrolytes.

Cool Down

This is the most commonly forgotten portion of the workout. It helps safely bring the body, heart rate, and muscles back to their resting state. Perform 5-10 minutes of low-intensity cardiovascular activity, followed by stretching. Cooling down immediately after your workout will help decrease delayed onset muscle soreness and aid in recovery which will help prepare your body for its next workout.

Don't Play When You're Injured

This is a really important one. If you love sports, it's tempting to get right back in the game, even after an injury. But playing when you're hurt or before an injury has had a chance to fully heal is a bad idea. It can lead to an even worse injury, one that might side-line you for a long time.

Resume activity slowly

Don't be tempted to nurse your injury for too long. Excessive rest may delay healing. After the initial 48-hour period of RICE, you can start using heat to help relax tight muscles. Take things slowly, and ease back in to exercise or your sport of choice.

Maintain flexibility

It is extremely important that you do dynamic stretches before starting your activity. Cold muscles are more prone to injury, so, while it may be tempting to start playing immediately, you should take a few minutes to do some jumping jacks, butt kicks, or arm circles first.

P.R.I.C.E.

Protection, Rest, Ice, Compression and Elevation, or P.R.I.C.E., adds the concept of "protection" to the traditional R.I.C.E. protocol formula.

Protecting the injured area from further damage is crucial to the healing process. Protect the injured person and the area being treated but also protect yourself. If the injury occurs on the sports field, stop the game.

Rehabilitation and Physiotherapy

Rehabilitation is care that can help you get back, keep, or improve abilities that you need for daily life. Physiotherapy helps through physical rehabilitation, injury prevention, and health and fitness. Physiotherapists get you involved in your own recovery. The terms "physiotherapy" and "physical therapy" mean the same thing and are used interchangeably, as are the terms “physiotherapist” and “physical therapist”. Physiotherapists have in-depth knowledge of how the body works and specialized hands-on clinical skills to assess, diagnose, and treat symptoms of illness, injury and disability. Physiotherapy is treatment to restore, maintain, and make the most of a patient’s mobility, function, and well-being. Physiotherapists work with clients of all ages and with a wide range of health conditions. Whether its pain management and rehabilitation from an acute injury like a sprained ankle or management of chronic conditions such as diabetes or heart disease, a physiotherapist can help. Physical therapy is provided by physical therapists who promote, maintain or restore the wellbeing through examination, diagnosis, prognosis, patient education, physiotherapeutic intervention, rehabilitation, disease prevention and health promotion.

Training Means for Development of Different Components of Physical Fitness

Speed

Speed in physical education is one of the most important fitness components, whether one plays sports or not, everyone wants speed because actions in everyday life situations need to be carried out at the appropriate speed to be able to achieve success. Speed has a direct relationship with the nervous system and the muscular system. Speed in physical education is considered a physical component. The brain and nervous system control and coordinate the movements of our muscles. Speed is defined as the ability to move the body in one direction as fast as possible. Speed is one of the main fitness components, important for success in many sports. Speed is important in sprinting, speed skating, sprint cycling and sports such as tennis when a player has to move forward quickly from the baseline to reach a drop shot close to the net.

Strength

Strength is one of the main fitness components, important for success in many sports. Certain sports, such as weight lifting, wrestling and weight throwing, it is the most important physical attribute. A strength exercise is any activity that makes your muscles work harder than usual. This increases your muscles' strength, size, power and endurance. The activities involve using your body weight or working against a resistance. Strength is the ability of a muscle to exert force in single muscle contraction or it is the ability to overcome resistance. Strength is an essential component of physical fitness. Strength refers to the quality or state of being strong. Our muscles are vital to our bodies and are the reasons we can walk, run, carry things, and so much more. But muscles start to deteriorate as we age, so finding ways such as resistance training to build muscle is crucial.

Endurance

Endurance is defined as the ability to continue despite fatigue or difficult conditions. The stamina to perform physical activities for longer periods of time can be improved by exercise and increasing the amount of activity. Endurance refers to an individual's ability to sustain physical activity or mental effort over an extended period. It is the capacity to withstand fatigue, stress, and discomfort while maintaining optimal performance levels. Endurance is a crucial aspect of athletic performance and overall fitness, enabling athletes to compete and excel in various sports. Endurance is the capacity of a person to work in unpleasant and hard situation without giving up. In physical education, endurance is explained as the capacity to work against fatigue. Endurance refers to your body's physical capability to sustain an exercise for an extended period. It's made up of two components: cardiovascular endurance and muscular endurance. Cardiovascular endurance is the ability of your heart and lungs to fuel your body with oxygen. Muscular endurance is the ability of your muscles to work continuously without getting tired.

Flexibility

Flexibility is an important part of physical fitness and is defined as the ability to move the joints freely. Both range of motion and mobility are common terms when discussing flexibility. Range of motion is how much a joint or body part can move and mobility is how easy it is to move. Flexibility can be assessed using various methods depending on the specific joints or muscle groups being evaluated. Flexibility helps performance, posture, promotes efficient movement, prevents incorrect body alignment, maintains appropriate muscle length and balance and also decreases injury risk. Flexibility is the ability to move muscles and joints through a full normal range of motion. Flexibility refers to the ability of muscles, joints, and soft tissues to move through an unrestricted, pain-free range of motion. It involves the capacity of these structures to stretch, lengthen, and contract without limitations, allowing for smooth and efficient movement.

Co-coordinative Abilities

Coordination is understood, in general terms, as the ability of the human body to unify in a synchronised manner the work of various muscles in the execution of an intentional action. Gross motor coordination involves the large muscles in your arms, legs, and torso, which you use for everyday activities like walking, lifting, throwing, running, and kicking. Fine motor coordination focuses on coordination of the small muscles in your hands and wrists the ones you use to write, type on your computer or phone, or do activities like sewing. Hand/eye coordination is the coordination of the information your eyes take in, and the signals your brain sends to your arms and hands. You rely on this to do everyday tasks like drive a car, cook, or pick up something. Coordination is the ability to select the right muscle at the right time with proper intensity to achieve proper action. Coordinated movement is characterized by appropriate speed, distance, direction, timing and muscular tension. Coordination is about our motor skills and can be broken up into fine or gross motor skills. Fine motor skills are about our coordination in relation to small movements and the ease they are performed. An example of a fine motor skill in sport is the snooker shot. Conversely, gross motor skills involve large movements and muscle groups. Examples of gross motor skills include walking, kicking, jumping and much more.

Practical Course

Course Code: PED304PR

Specialization in Athletics

UNIT-I

Introduction to Athletics

Athletics events and games are the oldest form of organized sport, having developed out of the most basic human activities, running, walking, jumping, and throwing. They are a truly international group of sports, with nearly every country in the world engaging in some form of competition. The objective depends on what the sport exactly is. In races, the objective is to run from the starting point to the destination before the opponents do. The word Athletics is derived from the Greek word 'ATHLON' which means competition and those who participated in such competitions came to be known as 'Athletes'. Although these contests are called track and field (or simply track) in the United States, they are generally designated as athletics elsewhere. Athletics is an exclusive collection of sporting events that involve competitive running, jumping, throwing, and walking. The most common types of athletics competitions are track and field, road running, cross country running, and race walking.

Historical Developmental of Athletics

In the year 776 BC in the ancient Olympia in Greece the first Olympic Games were held and during that games, only one, to use modern day terminology, track and field event was held and that was the stadium footrace and the winner of that events and the first ever Olympic winner was Koroibos. In 1896 first modern Olympic Games were held in Athens, Greece where athletics events were introduced. International Amateur Athletic Federation was established in 1912. The first Asian Track and Field tournament was held at Manila, Philippines in 1973. The first Ancient Greek Olympics in ancient Greece go back at least as far as the eighth or ninth century B.C. While such sports as boxing and equestrian events were included, most of the events were those now classified under athletics or track and field. They included common track events like running, both sprints and long distance running, jumping, discus and the javelin. Those four, plus wrestling, made up the pentathlon. In the 1960s, professional athletics began to emerge as a popular form of entertainment. The American Football League was founded in 1960, and in 1967 the first Super Bowl was played. Professional basketball and baseball also gained popularity during this time, with the founding of the American Basketball Association and the expansion of Major League Baseball. Athletics continues to evolve and grow in popularity around the world. New technologies and training methods are constantly being developed to help athletes reach new heights of performance. An athletics competition was included in the first modern Olympic Games in 1896 and it has been as one of the foremost competitions at the quadrennial multi-sport event ever since. Originally for men only, the 1928 Olympics saw the introduction of women's events in the athletics programme. Athletics is part of the Paralympic Games since the inaugural Games in 1960. Athletics has a very high-profile during major championships, especially the Olympics, but otherwise is less popular. An international governing body, the International Amateur Athletics Federation (IAAF), was founded in 1912; it adopted its current name, the International Association of Athletics Federations, in 2001. The IAAF established separate outdoor World Championships in 1983. In modern times, athletes can receive money for racing, putting an end to the so-called "amateurism" that existed before. By 2011, nearly 50 outdoor and 25 indoor events fall under the IAAF's authority and rules. Some events, such as the 50-meter sprint, are no longer part of major athletic competitions, but remain part of school programs. Some events have been modified through the years and races of many varying distances are contested every year.

Ancient Olympics

The Ancient Olympic Games were typically held for a duration of five days. The exact number of days could vary slightly between different editions of the Games, but generally, the event spanned multiple days to accommodate the various competitions and festivities associated with the Olympics. The Ancient Olympics were exclusively held in Olympia, a sanctuary located in Greece. The city of Olympia became the permanent venue for the Olympic Games, and athletes from various Greek city-states would gather there to compete. The Ancient Olympics featured a range of events that encompassed both individual and team sports. The competitions included various athletic contests such as running, jumping, throwing, wrestling, boxing, and chariot racing. The ancient Olympic Games were primarily a part of a religious festival in honour of Zeus, the father of the Greek gods and goddesses. The festival and the games were held in Olympia, a rural sanctuary site in the western Peloponnesos. Sadly, women were not allowed to compete at the Olympics. Married women were not even permitted to attend the Olympics as visitors. If women were caught trying to sneak into the games, they would be thrown off of Mount Olympus as punishment. Women had an equivalent festival called Heraean Games, which also took place in Olympia. The festival was held in honour of Zeus' wife, Hera. Women could take part in the foot race, but little else is known about the Heraean games as it did not acquire the same success as the Olympics. Ancient Olympic victors were treated like heroes. They were crowned with the *kotinos*, wore ribbons around their arms and heads, and held palm branches. They were carried on strong shoulders around the stadium, amidst frenzied cheers, all the way to their city where they thanked the gods and participated in public feasts. Their city-state often paid for statues or portraits in their honour and gave them substantial material rewards. An Athenian winner, for example, would receive up to 500 drachmas, an ancient Greek currency, and free meals at the city hall for life, while other honours included a lifetime pension and special seats at public events. The first known Olympics were held in the summer of 776 B.C. at Olympia, a site in southern Greece where people went to worship their gods. The Greeks that came to the Sanctuary of Zeus at Olympia shared the same religious beliefs and spoke the same language. The ancient Olympic Games, held every four years at Olympia in honour of the god Zeus, were celebrated for over a millennium and serve as the inspiration for the modern competition. The Olympic Games were the most important cultural event in ancient Greece and they ran for 293 consecutive Olympiads. So important were the Games in the ancient world that they were even used as a basis for the calendar. In ancient Greece, athletic competitions were organized first and foremost to honour the gods. Portraying courage, strength, and beauty was linked to high religious values. Some scholars suggest that competing naked was a way of honouring Zeus by presenting him a natural human form without ornaments or pretensions. Secondly, in ancient times war and conflict were never far away. For young Greek males, showing off a body that was strong, healthy, and ready for combat was part of their duty as citizens. Thirdly, Greeks considered themselves unashamedly better than anyone else. Because the athletes were naked, it could be easily seen that they were Greeks and not barbarians.

The events that were included in the Olympic Games were:-

1. Running races
2. Jumping
3. Discus
4. Javelin throwing
5. Boxing
6. Wrestling

Baron Pierre de Coubertin was inspired to found the International Olympic Committee (IOC). Coubertin presented the idea of conducting the Olympic Games during the first Olympic Congress of the newly created International Olympic Committee in 1894, at the University of Paris, which would internationally rotate between different countries. On the last day of the Congress, it was decided that the first Olympic Games, to be held under the auspices of the IOC, would take place in Athens in 1896. The most famous athletic competition in ancient Greece was the Olympic Games, which were held every four years in Olympia, in honour of the god Zeus. The Olympic Games were a religious festival, and the athletes had to swear an oath to compete fairly before the statue of Zeus.

Modern Olympics games

The Olympic Games are the biggest global celebration of sports. Every four years, this mega event gathers thousands of the best athletes in the world and attracts millions of viewers all over the globe. The Olympic Rings, which are considered the symbol of the Olympic Movement, represent Coubertin's dream. The symbol consists of five rings colored in blue, yellow, black, green and red. Baron de Coubertin became IOC president in 1896 and guided the Olympic Games through its difficult early years, when it lacked much popular support and was overshadowed by world's fairs. In 1924, the first truly successful Olympic Games were held in Paris, involving more than 3,000 athletes, including more than 100 women, from 44 nations. The first Winter Olympic Games were also held that year. In 1925, Coubertin retired. The Olympic Games have come to be regarded as the foremost international sports competition. The Olympic Games are widely regarded as the world's most prestigious sporting event, with more than 200 countries competing. Summer and Winter Olympic Games alternate every two years, making each event a four-year cycle. Inspired by the ancient

Olympic Games, which were held from the 8th century BC to the 4th century AD, their creation was based on the Olympic Games. The International Olympic Committee (IOC) was established in 1894 by Baron Pierre de Coubertin. Since then, the IOC has taken on the role of overseeing the entire Olympic Movement, as defined by the Olympic Charter. Today, the Olympics are divided into summer and winter sports. Summer Olympics and Winter Olympics are held on alternating even years, with each set of Olympics taking place every four years. For example Winter Olympics were held in 2022 and again in 2026. Summer Olympics will take place in 2024 and 2028. In modern Olympics, victors receive three medals gold for the winner, silver for the first runner-up, and bronze for the second runner-up which translate into cash prizes. The Summer Olympics is a much bigger competition and includes events such as athletics (or 'track and field'), swimming, diving, boxing, wrestling, cycling, basketball, sailing, rowing, football, hockey, tennis, equestrian, shooting, weightlifting, gymnastics, etc. It occurs every four years. The Winter Olympics includes events such as skiing, ski jumping, speed skating, figure skating, ice hockey, curling, bob sleigh, etc. The Winter Olympics also occurs every four years (but separated from the Summer Olympics by two years). In the modern era, the Olympic Games have expanded to include a wide range of sports in both the summer and winter seasons, attracting tens of thousands of athletes. The Olympic Hymn is the official anthem of the Olympic Games. Its lyrics were written by the renowned Greek poet Kostis Palamas and composed by the Greek musician Spiros Samaras. It was performed for the first time during the opening ceremony of the 1896 Games, in Athens. However, it wasn't until 1958 that it was declared the official hymn by the IOC. Each Olympic Games host city has its own mascot: a pet or a figure which represents the Games values. Some famous mascots from the Olympic Games history include Micha from the 1980 Games in Moscow and Cobi from the 1992 Games in Barcelona.

Historical review of track and field with special reference to India

Track and field has been around since the start of the Olympics in Ancient Greece in 776 B.C. It was created alongside religious events and celebrations for the Greek gods where men (no women were allowed) could show off their athletic abilities. While track and field has a long and storied history, it did not gain great popularity and take off until the 1860s. In 1866,

England held its first championships for men amateurs. Specific track events include indoor and outdoor sprints. Indoor sprints range from 50 yards to 500 meters and outdoor sprints are either 100, 200, or 400 meters. Middle distance races range from 800 to 2,000 meters and long distances range from 3,000 to 30,000 meters. India's first brush with the Olympics came at the 1900 Paris Olympics - where Norman Pritchard was the country's sole representative. He won two silver medals - in the 200m sprint and 200m hurdles. The first multi-sport Olympic contingent for India came at the Antwerp 1920 Olympics - where five athletes (three in athletics and two wrestlers) took part. At the Paris 1924 Olympics, India made their tennis debut. Five players (4 male and 1 female) played in the singles events. Two pairs played the men's doubles and one in the mixed doubles. At Tokyo 2020, Neeraj Chopra clinched India's first-ever athletics medal, that too gold, at the Olympics, thereby shifting the country's focus on track and field events in a big way. Neeraj Chopra's gold-winning throw of 87.58m, however, wasn't his personal best or the national record for Indian javelin.

National and International level athletics championships:-

Olympic Games

The Olympic Games are a symbol of national pride and unity, and it is held every four years to uphold world peace and develop brotherhood between nations. Athletes and players endure years of hard work and dedication to participate in the Olympic Games. They train rigorously and present their abilities during a qualifying round, after which they will be chosen for the Olympic Games. The Olympic Games are an important event in the international sports world. The foremost sporting event sees participation by athletes from more than 200 countries. In addition to sports fans, millions worldwide see the live telecast of the Olympics games and its awards ceremonies. The goal of the Olympic Movement is to contribute to building a peaceful and better world by educating youth through sport practiced without discrimination of any kind and in the Olympic spirit, which requires mutual understanding with a spirit of friendship, solidarity and fair play.

Asian games

The Asian Games is a multi-disciplinary sports event held once in every four years. Athletes from all Asian countries are welcomed to participate in this event. The Asian Games is recognised by the International Olympic Committee and is the second largest multi-sport event after the Olympics.

IAAF-World Championship

The World Athletics Championships (until 2019 known as the IAAF World Championships in Athletics) are a biennial athletics competition organized by World Athletics (formerly IAAF, International Association of Athletics Federations).

Commonwealth Games

Since 2000, the Commonwealth Games have been complemented by the Commonwealth Youth Games, involving athletes aged 14 to 18. The Commonwealth Games is an international sporting event held every four years in which different teams from Commonwealth countries can participate. Apart from 1942 and 1946, during and immediately after World War II, it has been continuously held since 1930. Today, the Commonwealth Games have grown to an event consisting of 70 nations and territories, with over 6,600 athletes and team officials. In April 2018, Australia hosted the 21st Commonwealth Games on the Gold Coast. Following Sydney (1932), Perth (1962), Brisbane (1982) and Melbourne (2006), 2018 was the fifth time Australia has hosted the Games making Australia the nation that has hosted the most Commonwealth Games. There have been six editions so far in non-Games years, most recently in 2017 in Nassau in The Bahamas.

National Games

The National Games of India is an Olympic-style multi-sport event where athletes from the various states and Union Territories of India compete for medals. Services, the sports team of the Indian Armed Forces, also compete at the National Games. At the National Games 2022, athletes competed in 36 sports, including non-Olympic ones like kabaddi, kho kho, lawn bowls, mallakhamb, squash, wushu and yogasana.

Open National Athletics Championships

The Indian National Open Athletics Championships is an annual outdoor track and field competition organised by the Athletics Federation of India, which serves as the national championship for the sport in India.

Youth National Athletics Championships

The Oceania Youth Athletics Championships is an athletics event organized by the Oceania Athletics Association open for youth (U18) athletes from member and associate member associations.

Inter-Universities Athletics Championships

The Competitions shall be conducted as per the Regulations of the IAAF Rules and events as existing in the World University Games. Each University shall pay the officiating fee of Rs. 3000 per team (men and women separately) at the time of registration.

UNIT-II

Athletic track and its Types

A standard track is of 400 m distance with eight to ten lanes. Track can be laid on various types of surfaces like clay, grass, cinder and synthetic (tartan), etc. Track is the place where an athlete competes against time, thus it is an oval place where an athlete performs different running events like Sprints, Middle distance, Long distance and Obstacle races etc.

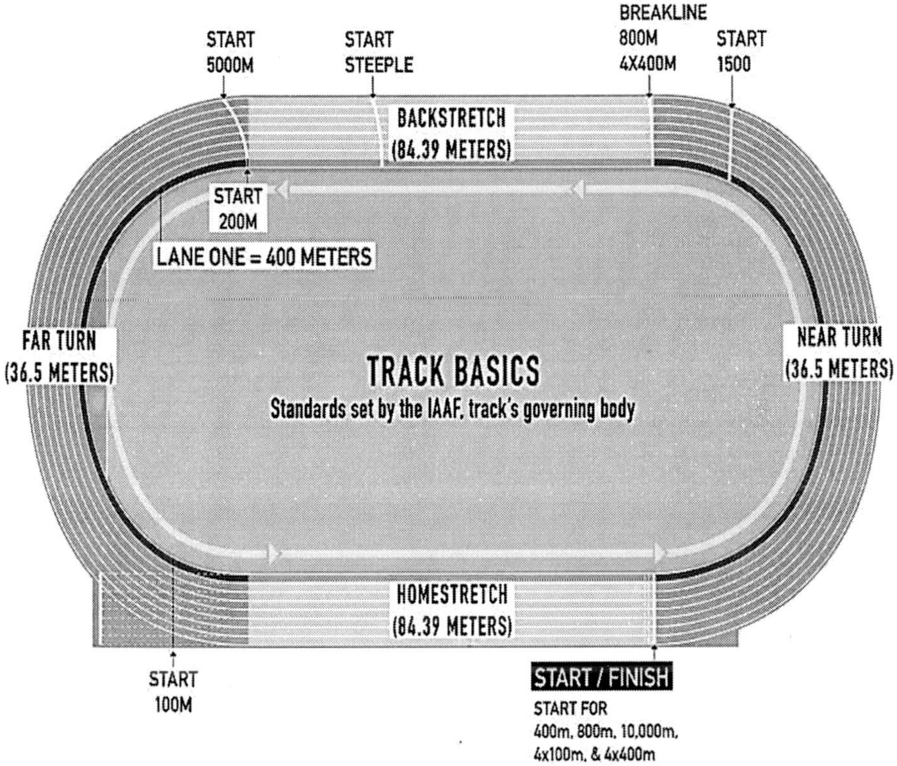

All athletics running tracks should be appropriately line marked with weather-resistant paint to ensure that the staggered starting lines are marked accurately and therefore all competitors in a race will run the same distance. Track events include sprint, middle distance, hurdle and steeplechase events. The 400m oval track forms the basis of a multi-sports arena and its dimensions are dependent on the requirements of other sports.

There are several types of running track surfaces available. Each of them comes with its advantages and disadvantages.

- Clay and Cinder
- Grass and Turf
- Asphalt
- Synthetic
- Latex track surfaces
- Polyurethane track surfaces

Procedure and methods to mark the track (200m, 400m)

The 200 metres, or 200-meter dash, is a sprint running event. On an outdoor 400 metre racetrack, the race begins on the curve and ends on the home straight, so a combination of techniques is needed to successfully run the race.

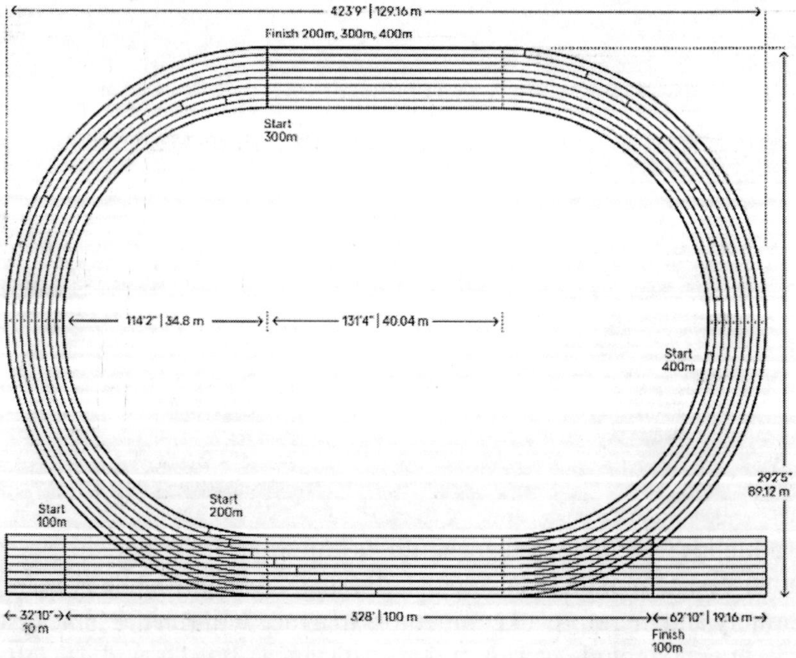

Marking and construction of Shot Put Arena

The shot put playing area includes a stop/toe board, a throwing circle and a landing area for the shot.

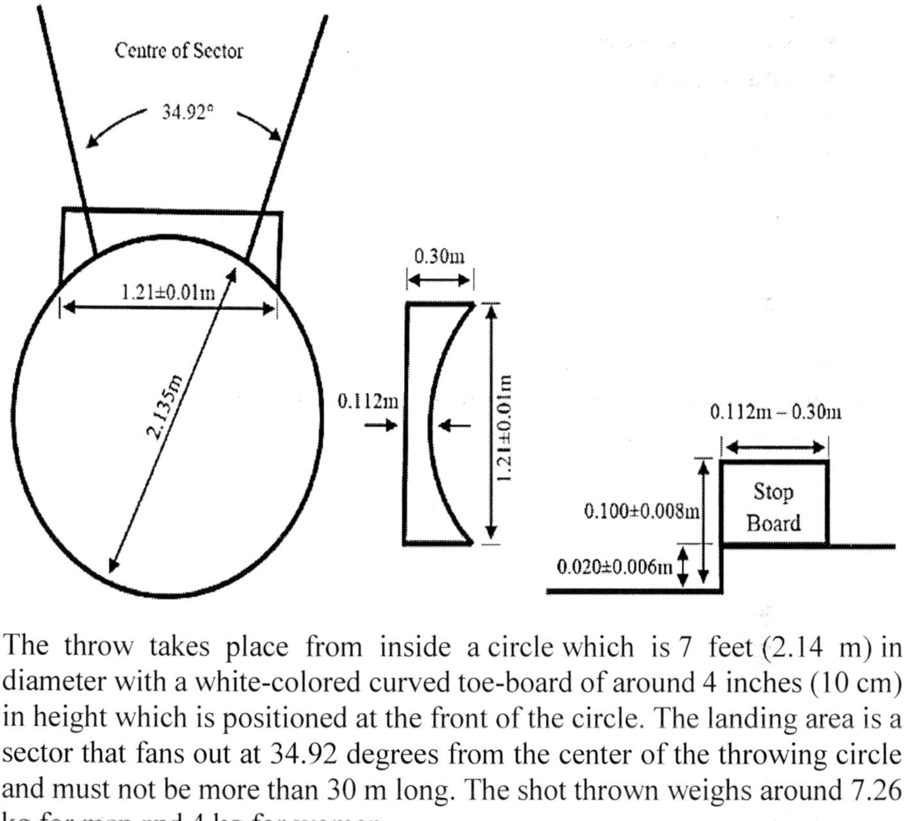

The throw takes place from inside a circle which is 7 feet (2.14 m) in diameter with a white-colored curved toe-board of around 4 inches (10 cm) in height which is positioned at the front of the circle. The landing area is a sector that fans out at 34.92 degrees from the center of the throwing circle and must not be more than 30 m long. The shot thrown weighs around 7.26 kg for men and 4 kg for women.

Marking and construction of Discus Throw Arena

To have a perfect throw, the athlete has to start throwing from a throwing circle of 2.5 m (8 ft. 2 ¼ in.) in diameter, which is made up of concrete or some non-slippery material. The throwing circle is enclosed with a rim of 6 mm thickness and a depth of 70 to 80 mm. The landing zone (also called landing sector) is where the discus arrives after the athlete throws it. The landing zone's surface is made of natural grass or other smooth suitable material. The landing zone is laid at an angle of 34.92 degree with respect to the middle of the throwing circle. It is marked by 50 mm wide white lines and the landing zone is 80 m long.

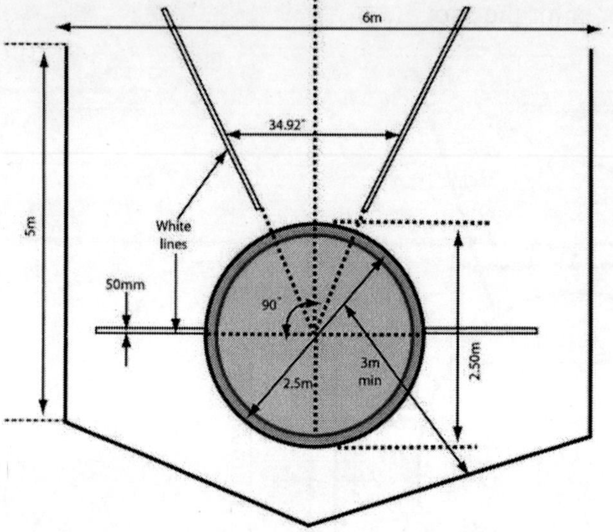

Marking and construction of Javelin throw Arena

The runway or take-off area is a stretch of running track which allows javelin throwers to make a running start before their throw and gather momentum before releasing the javelin.

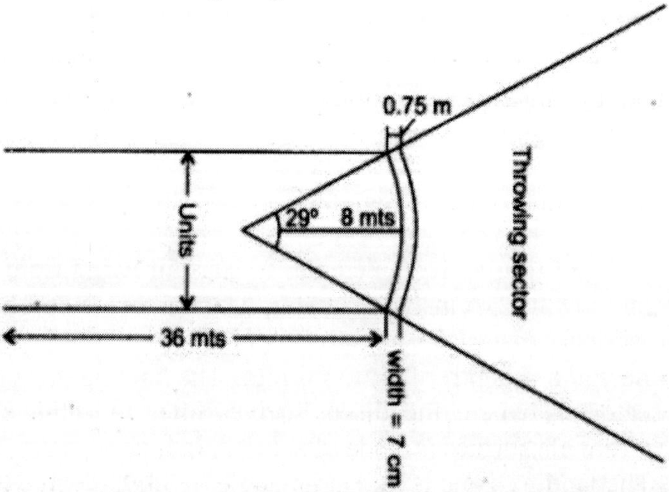

The runway should at least be 30 metres in length and can extend to 36.50 metres, if conditions permit. The minimum width of a runway must be 4 metres. The end of the runway is marked by the throwing arc, which has an 8 metres radius. The throwing arc is also called the foul line or scratch line. Athletes cannot step beyond the runway markings once their attempt starts.

Marking and construction of Hammer throw Arena

For men, the hammer has a minimum mass of 7.260 kg, the cable a maximum length of 121.5 cm and the sphere a diameter between 11 cm and 13 cm. For women, the mass is 4 kg minimum, the length 119.5 cm maximum and the diameter between 9.5 cm and 11 cm.

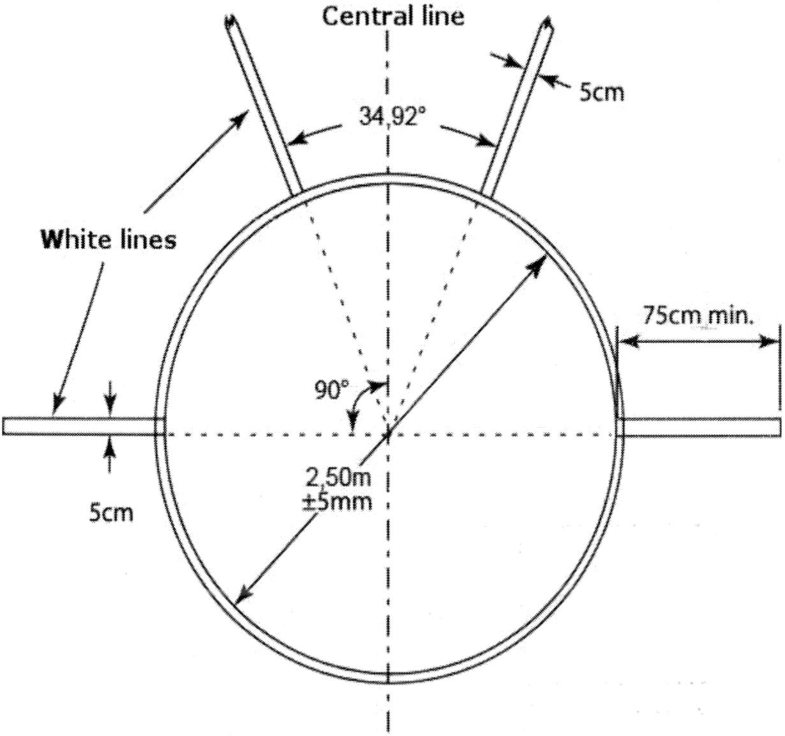

Specification and construction of Long Jump pit/runways

The runway for long jump is about forty meters long and 1.22 m (4 ft.) in width. The takeoff board is a white colored rectangular piece of wood that is 1.22 m (4 ft.) in length and is twenty centimeter (7.87 in.) in width and ten centimeter (3.93 in.) in depth.

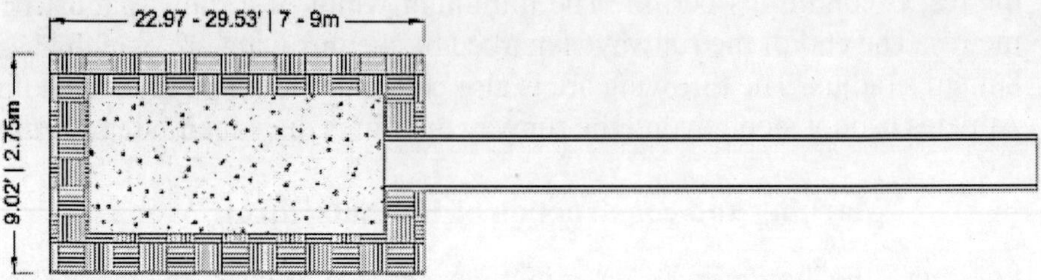

The plasticine is placed at least one meter from the landing area to determine the fault takeoffs which is commonly red in color. The landing Area is filled with silicon sand which is commonly 2.75 meters (9 ft.) in width, nine meters (29.52 ft.) in length and at least thirty centimeters (11.81 in.) in depth.

Specification and construction of Triple Jump pit/runways

The runway for Triple jump is about forty meters long and 1.22 m (4 ft.) in width. The take-off board is a white colored rectangular piece of wood that is 1.22 m (4 ft.) in length and is twenty centimetre (7.87 in.) in width and ten centimetre (3.93 in.) in depth. The plasticine is placed at least 13 meters (42.7 feet) from the landing area for men and 11 meters (36 feet) for women to determine the fault take-offs which are commonly red in color.

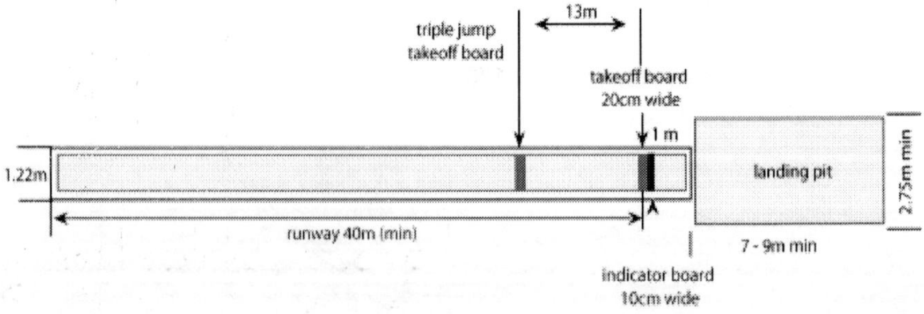

The Landing Area is filled with silicon sand which is commonly 2.75 meters (9 ft.) in width, nine meters (29.52 ft.) in length and at least thirty centimetres (11.81 in.) in depth.

Specification and construction of High jump pit/runways

The semicircular runway, with a radius of at least 20m, will permit approaches from every direction. If it is necessary to remove the kerb temporarily in order to be able to use the oval track as a runway, care must be taken to ensure that the heights of the surfaces of the oval track and the segment are the same along the track border.

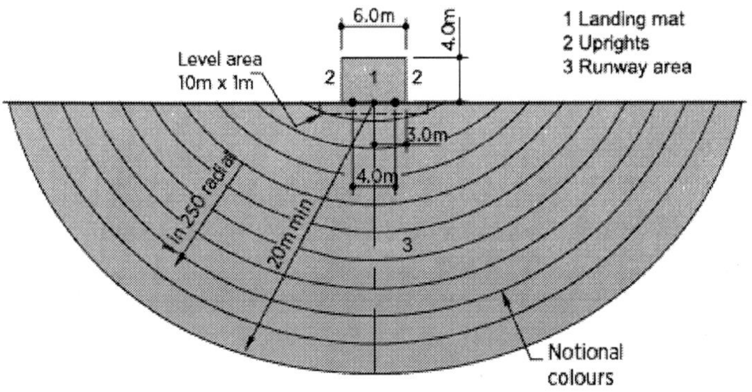

The runway and take-off areas are usually covered with the same surface as the track.

Specification and construction of Pole vault pit/runways

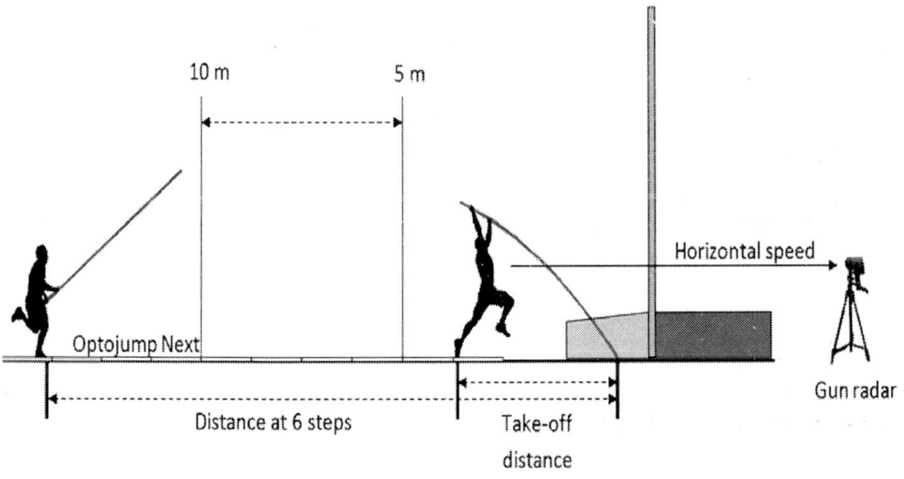

Selected National and International personalities in athletics

Jyotirmayee Sikdar

Jyotirmayee Sikdar has been an Indian athlete and brought glory to the country by winning the gold medal in the Bangkok Asian Games 1998. Sikdar first came into limelight when she made her national athletics debut in the year 1992 at the All India Open Meet. In her first national level athletics meet, she was successful in winning a silver medal in the 800 meters race. The very next year, Jyotirmoyee won the gold medal at the Open National Athletics Meet 1993. In the year 1994, she created a new national record and won the gold medal in the 1500 meters race event at the National Athletics Meet. She also set a new national record in the 800 meters race in 1995.

Soma Biswas

Soma Biswas is an athlete who lives in Kolkata, India and specializes in heptathlon. She rose to fame when she won a silver medal at the 2002 Asian Games in Busan, South Korea. She won another silver medal at the 2006 Asian Games in Doha. She managed to win the 110 m hurdles, 200 m and 800 m during that heptathlon. Biswas worked with Kuntal Rai and many foreign coaches.

Sunil Gavaskar

Sunil Manohar Gavaskar is a former Indian cricketer, born on 10 July 1949 in then Bombay, now Mumbai. Sunil Manohar Gavaskar Right-handed batsman kept the Indian fort at the top against poor fast bowling in the 1970s and 1980s. Gavaskar was the first batsman to scale the mountain of 10000 runs in Tests and had the most Test tons (34) until Sachin Tendulkar surpassed the tally. He was part of the 1983 World Cup winning team. Sunil Gavaskar was also the captain of the Indian cricket team for some time, but his record as captain was not very impressive, because all the matches played under his leadership were drawn. He led the team in 47 Test matches, of which they won 9, lost 8 and drew 30.

Chetan Anand

Chetan Anand's early association with badminton was through his father Harshvardhan Anand, who participated in inter-state lecturer tournaments. Gradually Chetan started joining him. As soon as he started playing, he realized how much he enjoyed the game. His ability was prominent to his father who encouraged him to pursue it. Chetan Anand soon became a classic stroke player. Chetan Anand made his debut in the international badminton arena in the year 2002, when he was a member of the Indian badminton team that participated in the Thomas Cup tournament. He reached the quarterfinal round of the India Asia Satellite Tournament in the same year and the quarterfinal round of the Australia Ballarat International Tournament 2003. In the year 2004, he again reached the quarterfinal round of the Indian Asian Satellite Tournament. He received the prestigious Arjuna Award in 2006.

P.V. Sindhu

PV Sindhu is an Indian badminton player who is the first Indian woman to win a silver medal in an international competition. Sindhu is the first Indian woman to win a World Championship and the first Indian woman to reach the final of the World Badminton Championships. P.V. Sindhu brought honor to her country by winning the bronze medal in Tokyo Olympics 2021. She represented India at the 2016 Summer Olympics in Rio, where she made Olympic history as the first badminton player from her country to do so. At the 2020 Summer Olympics (Tokyo), she competed for the second consecutive time and finished second, losing to Carolina Marin of Spain. She won a silver medal and created history by becoming the first Indian woman to win two Olympic medals.

Mouma Das

Mouma Das is a famous Indian table tennis athlete. Her date of birth was 24 February 1984. Her place of birth was Kolkata, India. She has won several awards in the Commonwealth Games and achieved victory status in the Women's Team Competition, 2018. Das has received the Arjuna Award and the Padma Shri, both the highest prestigious awards, for his contribution to sports. In the early stages of her career, Mouma was trained by Jayant Pusilal. Apart from Jayant, Mouma was also guided by Germany's Peter Engel, who helped sustain the table tennis player's success. In 2012, Mouma Das married Kanchan Chakraborty. In 2015, Das earned a silver medal in the singles category and also in the team event at the Commonwealth Championships. With these achievements, the table tennis player became the maximum Commonwealth medal holder from India. In 2015, Mouma qualified for the Rio Olympics 2016 at the Asian Qualification in Hong

Kong. Unfortunately at the Olympics, Das lost in the first round (women's individual event) to higher seeded player Daniela Dodian of Romania.

Dilip Tirkey

Dilip Tirkey is a former professional Indian field hockey player, politician and sports administrator. Dilip played as a full-back for the Indian hockey team and was widely known as the "Wall of Indian Hockey". He is the first and only player to play more than 400 matches for India. He represented India in three Olympic Games and also led the team at the 2004 Summer Olympics in Athens.

Gagan Ajit Singh

Gagan Ajit Singh is an Indian hockey player and a skilled striker on the field. He is the son of veteran Indian hockey player Ajit Singh, who represented the Indian hockey team at the Munich Olympic Games 1972 and Montreal Olympic Games 1976. Gagan's uncle, Harmik Singh, has also been an Indian hockey player and captain. He made his international debut in 1997 during the Test series against Russia. He then participated in the 1998 Commonwealth Games held in Kuala Lumpur, the 1999 tour of South Africa, 14 European tours from 1999 to 2004, 10 Australian tours from 1999 to 2004 and the India-Pakistan series 1999, where he scored 17 goals. India's highest scorer against the opposition. He also played in the 2000 Sultan Azlan Shah Cup tournament held in Kuala Lumpur, the 2001 Champions Challenge tournament and the 2001 New Zealand tour, where he scored 4 goals including a hat-trick. Singh played for India in the 2000 and 2004 Summer Olympics; India was ranked 7th on both the occasions.

Dhyanchand

A legend of Indian hockey, Dhyan Chand is considered one of the best players to have played the game. Major Dhyan Chand, the Indian hockey legend is known for his goal scoring ability which made him history by winning three gold medals in three consecutive Olympic events. The eminent personality has served in the army as well as on the hockey field throughout his life. Widely regarded as the magician of hockey, this man had scored almost 1000 goals in his active career which is a record achievement. Dhyan Chand performed brilliantly in the first inter-provincial (national) hockey tournament held in the year 1925. United Provinces (UP), Punjab, Bengal, Rajputana and Central Provinces participated in the tournament. Based on his performance in the tournament, he was selected for the India international hockey team. In the year 1926, Dhyan Chand was selected for the Indian hockey team going on the tour of New Zealand. During the tour, the Indian team scored 20 goals in a match played in Dunkerque and 10 of them were scored by Dhyanchand alone. India played 21 matches on the tour, out of which it won 18, lost 1 and drew 2. The team scored a total of 192 goals and Dhyan Chand alone had scored more than 100 of them.

Need, importance and procedure of Warming-up and Cooling down

A warm up should include multiple dynamic exercises increasing in intensity as you get closer to the workout. Dynamic exercises provide a stretch through full range of motion, but the stretch is not held in the ending position.

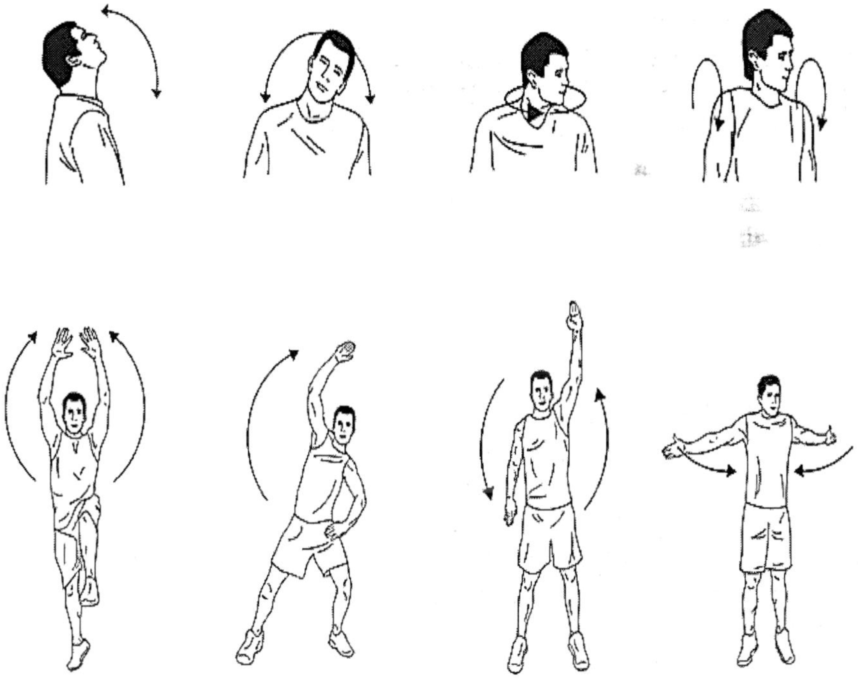

Static stretches or stretches that are held in the ending position are not ideal for a warm up, due to the stop of blood flow to the muscle. Static stretches should be performed after a workout as part of a cool down. They are great for increasing flexibility, but are not supportive to the meaning of a warm up. The warm-up should gently prepare the body for exercises by gradually increasing the heart rate and circulation; this will loosen the joints and increase blood flow to the muscles. Stretching the muscles prepares them for physical activity and prevents injuries. The warm-up is also a good opportunity for an individual to prepare themselves mentally for the game ahead and for a team to work together prior to the start of the game. A warm-up also activates and primes the connections between your nerve and muscles, which improves the efficiency of movement. Additionally, your range of motion (flexibility) should be increased by dynamic stretching. Warm-ups can also be used to practice skills and team drills. The purpose of warming up before physical activity is to prepare mentally and physically for your chosen activity. Warming up increases your heart rate and therefore your blood flow which enables more oxygen to reach your muscles. A warmup gradually revs up your cardiovascular system by raising your body temperature and increasing blood flow to your muscles. Warming up may also help reduce muscle soreness and lessen your risk of injury. A warm-up is a short activity or exercise undertaken prior to a more intensive exercise or activity. A warm-up is intended to prepare the body for movement, including exercise, sport, dance, and stretching. The warm up exercises are crucial to any sports or fitness training program. The importance of a structured warm up routine should not be under estimated when it comes to preventing sports injury. A proper warm up has a number of very important key components. Warming up helps prepare your body for aerobic activity.

A cool down is an essential part of your workout. A cool down can last for 3–10 minutes and includes stretches or gentle variations of the movements you did during your workout. The purpose of cooling down after exercise is to allow your heart rate and breathing to return to normal and to promote relaxation. Cooling down after your workout allows for a gradual recovery of pre exercise heart rate and blood pressure. Cooling down may be most important for competitive endurance athletes, such as marathoners, because it helps regulate blood flow. Cooling down doesn't appear to help reduce muscle stiffness and soreness after exercise, but more research is needed. Cooling down after a workout is as important as warming up. After physical activity, your heart is still beating faster than normal, your body temperature is higher and your blood vessels are dilated.

First Aid and Rehabilitation of Athletics Injuries

First aid is an emergency measure, generally consisting of simple, often life-saving techniques that most people can train to perform with minimal equipment and no previous medical experience. The term usually refers to administering care to a human, although it can also be performed on animals. Using personal protective gear is an important strategy to minimize the risk of blood and bodily fluid exposure. If the person is bleeding, always wear gloves and protective eyewear when giving first aid care. The universal precaution is to use personal protective equipment whenever there is possible exposure to blood or bodily fluids; it reduces the risk for both the rescuer and the injured/ill person to be exposed to a blood-borne disease. Gloves protect your hands from exposure to blood and other bodily fluids, while eye protection prevents accidental exposure from splashing fluids. First aid covers the steps taken to help a person in the first minutes of an illness or injury. Accidents or illness can happen to anyone at any time, whether at home, at work or at school. First aid refers to medical attention that is usually administered immediately after the injury occurs and at the location where it occurred. It often consists of a one-time, short-term treatment and requires little technology or training to administer. First aid is vital for saving lives. A person can carry out first aid after a life-threatening incident or injury before the arrival of emergency services. When you provide basic medical care to someone experiencing a sudden injury or illness, it's known as first aid. In some cases, first aid consists of the initial support provided to someone in the middle of a medical emergency. This support might help them survive until professional help arrives. Rehabilitation is care that can help you get back, keep, or improve abilities that you need for daily life.

UNIT-III

Brief background of Track Events:-

A track event is an event in athletics that requires the athlete to run or walk around a track. Track events mainly consist of activities which test an athlete's running, endurance, agility, and speed capabilities. Some popular track events include the long distance run, the middle distance run, short distance sprints, relay races, and steeplechase races. The number of track and field events at each competition varies. Scoring also varies between national and international competitions. Some popular forms of track and field events are the heptathlon and the decathlon, which feature seven and ten events respectively.

Technique, training and important motor components of the following track events:-

Sprints races: 100m, 200m, 400m
Sprint events in track and field usually consists of the 100m, 200m and 400m race though 60m dashes are also held on occasion. The sprints are among the oldest running competitions and are said to have evolved from the 180m stadion race held during the ancient Olympic games.

100m

- The race starts with a command: "on your mark" followed by "set" and then the gun is fired.
- The runners accelerate up to between the 40m and 60m marks, when they reach top speed.

200m

- In the 200m races, runners only use 92 to 93 percent of their maximum speed.
- They reach their highest speed between the 100m and 150m marks.
- The time is registered when the runner's torso (chest) passes the finish line.
- That is the reason why most athletes lunge forward when they approach the finish line.

400m

- In the race, after the acceleration phase, it is important for the sprinters to run in as relaxed a mode as possible up to the 250-300m mark, when the lactid acid starts building up.
- From then on, the aim is to lose as little as possible.
- The best lanes are 3,4,5 and 6.
- The bends for the athletes in the inner lanes are tight while those in outer lanes can't see their competitors.
- The 400m is a lot about sprint endurance and the runners undergo a lot of lactic acid training in order to cope with the last 100m of the race.

Hurdle Races

Hurdling is a type of jumping in which an athlete jumps over an obstacle at a high speed or in a sprint. Hurdling is a highly specialized form of obstacle racing that is part of the sport of athletics. Moreover, the hurdling events, barriers or obstacles are known as hurdles that are set at a defined distance according to the event.

1) On Your Marks: At this point the athlete is focused on the track, with his / her feet placed in the blocks and fingers on the ground behind the starting line. Note: The hands should be placed such that they are slightly away from the shoulder width with muscles relaxed.
2) Set: On the "set" command, athletes raise their hips a little higher than the shoulders. In this position the runner concentrates deeply and holds the breath so that he can propel his body forward at the start.
3) Go: After the pistol is fired, the runner lets out his breath and he moves his arms and legs in such a way that the body propels forward at a forty-five degree angle until the back leg is fully extended.

Steeple Chase

A steeplechase race is a track race that takes runners over 28 large, fixed barriers and seven water jumps. It's important to note that this isn't a normal hurdles race steeplechase uses large barriers that span several lanes. Unlike hurdle races, steeplechase barriers don't move from their positions if they're hit by a runner, Barreau pointed out. They're also much larger than hurdles, spanning several lanes on the track.

Middle and Long Distance Races

Middle Distance and Long Distance running races are the track running events which take place over standard distances. Middle Distance includes 800 meters and 1,500 meters while the Long Distance includes 5,000 meters, 10,000 meters and 3,000 meters steeplechase event. The athletes begin both the races without the starting blocks. In the 800 m final, the 8 runners run in the assigned lanes throughout the first curve (lap) and then break for the inside lane after the end of the first curve. In the 1500 m final, a maximum of 12 runners line up on the starting line that is curved so that the athletes on the outside of the track run the equal distance as the athletes placed closer to the inside. The two main techniques used in these events are that some athletes try to front-run the entire race or some athletes depend on their finishing kick.

Combined Events

Combined events at the Summer Olympics have been contested in several formats at the multi-sport event. There are two combined track and field events in the current Olympic athletics programme: a men's decathlon (100 metres, long jump, shot put, high jump, 400 metres, 110 metres hurdles, discus throw, pole vault, javelin throw, and 1500 metres) and a women's heptathlon (100 metres hurdles, high jump, shot put, 200 metres, long jump, javelin throw, and 800 metres).

Decathlon and Hepthalon

The decathlon (men) and heptathlon (women) are sporting events fought with a combination of running, jumping, and throwing events. The winners are crowned with the titles of the King of Athletes and the Queen of Athletes, respectively. When it comes to distance running, a marathon is often one of the first distances that comes to mind, and the goal of completing one is something many runners aspire to.

Relay Races and Marathon

A marathon relay is a relay race that covers the full marathon distance 26.2 miles or 42.195 kilometers. Like other relay race events, a marathon relay involves a team of runners running different legs of the race, one after the next, passing a baton or otherwise tagging the next runner into the race after each runner's portion of the race is done.

Brief background of Fields Events

A field event is an athletics contest such as the high jump or throwing the discus or javelin, rather than a race.

Technique, training and important motor components of the following field events:-

Shot put

- Glide Shot Put

This technique was invented by Parry O'Brien from United States in 1952. This technique not only gave him an extra quarter-turn but also increased his propulsion and improved his performance by about 1 meter.

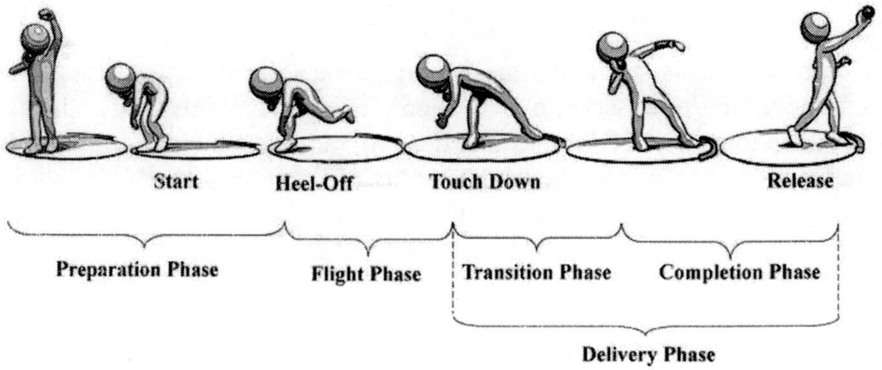

Steps

1. The athlete needs to be relaxed while all of his body weight is on his leading leg (that is slightly in front of other) with the strongest arm (depends on the player whether left-handed or right-handed) holding the shot put on the side of the neck under the chin.
2. The athlete has to lift its supporting leg behind the leading leg knee with the supporting arm in front of the chest.
3. Now, the athlete stretches out the supporting leg while pushing off the leading leg with the hips in rotation.
4. The last and important step is that the athlete locks its leg while facing the landing area (target) and pushes the ball / shot powerfully engaging the shoulder and chest muscles. The sudden extension of the putting arm propels the shot.

➢ Spin Shot Put

This technique was first used by Aleksandr Baryshnikov in 1972 and was invented by his coach Viktor Alexeyev. It involves a spin just like discus throw with the help of rotational momentum for power.

Steps

1. In this technique the athlete stands side on to the marker, while bringing the supporting arm across body and bends the back knee sideways.
2. The leading arm rotates around the body as the free arm is straight with the back leg leaning further to get the maximal power.
3. As the hips thrust forward with the shot put touching the neck meanwhile the arm swings round to get prepared to push the shot put.
4. Now, push the shot put forward, using legs and shoulder power while landing over the previously bent leg with arms and body in rotation.

Discus throw

Gripping the Discus

The athlete has to place the hand flat on the discus such that it is held with the fingers spread slightly and thumb used for balance.

Swing

In a swinging or rhythmic action, the athlete moves the discus back and forth in motion to gain momentum with his shoulders, arms relaxed and concentrates deeply.

Spin

During a one and a half turn rotation, the athlete's body accumulates as much energy as possible and he / she pushes powerfully off the **left leg** (If right-handed), while the left arm acts as a counter-weight along the axis of the shoulders.

Drive

Up to the last moment, the trunk and arms are extended with the hips, legs and feet in motion.

Release

Using the right leg as lever the athlete quickly straightens the body and thus the discus is thrown in an explosive motion with the arms moving around.

Javelin throw

- Approach run

Athletes gain momentum by running over a short distance. In the last few strides, the athletes cross legs in preparation for getting maximum torque on the throw. At last, they untwist the legs and pull back the throwing arm and push the other arm forward to help their aim and follow-through.

- Grip

The Javelin must be held with its grip and horizontally in the palm with the palm facing up always. There are three main styles of gripping:-
Finnish Grip- Gripping the cord between the thumb and the middle finger
American Grip- Gripping the cord between the thumb and the index finger
Fork Style Grip- Gripping the cord between the index and the middle finger

- Launch and Release

Just before throwing the Javelin, the athlete keeps the Javelin behind his/her shoulders for as long as possible, then stops suddenly and thrusts the throwing arm forward to achieve the greatest possible speed of throw.

Hammer Throw
The hammer throw involves a heavy ball attached to a strong wire. The ball is swung twice in the same spot, legs stationary. Next, you make three or four rotations with your body in a circular motion, with your feet engaged in a heel-toe movement. Then, you release the ball into the designated zone. Whoever can throw the hammer the furthest, wins the event.

Long Jump

- The approach

The objective is to progressively accelerate to a maximum speed for takeoff. The chief factor for maximising the distance traveled by an object is its velocity and flight angle at takeoff.

- The take-off

The take-off is the transition from the final step to being airborne. An athlete needs to ensure that their foot is flat on the ground to have optimum impact as jumping off either the heels or the toes has adverse impacts on the jump.

- Kick

The kick style takeoff is a style of takeoff where the athlete actively cycles the leg before a full impulse has been directed into the board then landing into the pit.

- Double-arm

The double-arm style of takeoff works by moving both arms in a vertical direction as the competitor takes off. This produces a high hip height and a large vertical impulse.

- Sprint

The sprint takeoff is the style most widely instructed by coaching staff. This is a classic single-arm action that resembles a jumper in full stride. It is an efficient takeoff style for maintaining velocity through takeoff.

- Power sprint or bounding

The power sprint or bounding takeoff is very similar to the sprint style, but there is one major difference. The arm that pushes back on takeoff (the arm on the side of the takeoff leg) fully extends backward, rather than remaining at a bent position. This additional extension increases the impulse at takeoff.

- Sail

The most basic one of the lot, the sail involves the jumper immediately lifting their legs into a toe-touching position after take-off. This allows the body to float or sail in the air longer with the momentum achieved during take-off.

- Hang

This technique involves stretching the body and making it as long as possible after being airborne. Both arms and legs are extended to reach the maximum distance possible and the position is maintained until the jumper reaches the highest elevation. At the apex, the jumper shifts their legs forward into a landing position.

- Hitch-kick

Also called climbing or running in the air, the athletes rotate their arms and legs during the flight to maintain balance. This is the most complex of the three techniques.

- Landing

While landing, a long jumper's objective is to glide into the sand-pit rather than just dropping in it. To ensure the closest indention to the take-off board made by their body is at the maximum distance possible, an athlete can turn to several manoeuvres while landing.

Triple Jump

Approach

This is arguably the most important part of a triple jump. The athlete sprints down the runway to the take-off line, which is where the jump is measured from. This part is important as they need to maintain a good speed throughout the whole jump.

Hop

This part of the jump begins when the athlete leaves the take-off mark on one foot, and propels themselves forwards with as much momentum as possible.

Step

When the athlete lands the hop stage, the step stage begins. They have to use the momentum from the hop to jump forwards and upwards. They should pull their leg up as high as possible to make the furthest jump they can.

Jump

When the athlete's step has landed, they move onto the jump. This part is very similar to the long jump, and they will land in a sandpit as they finish. The jumper should try not to sit backwards or place their hands behind their feet in the sandpit after they land to help with measuring the distance.

High Jump

- Scissors Technique

The scissors high jump technique was initially utilized by early jumpers in the 19th century. Nowadays, this introductory technique is commonly employed by young athletes to build their confidence, as it is both user-friendly and accessible. During the scissors high jump, athletes execute a straight thirty-degree angle run towards the bar. Subsequently, they navigate over the bar by placing their nearest leg first, followed by the other leg. The primary objective of the scissors technique is for athletes to land in a standing position on their feet on the mats.

- Eastern Cut-Off Technique

In the eastern cut-off technique the athlete rotates the trunk into a horizontal position at the peak of a jump. The athlete lifts the pelvis part higher than the simple scissors technique. This ultimately results in a higher bar clearance. The only draw-back of this technique is that this requires tremendous flexibility for higher jump.

- Western Roll Technique

In the western roll technique, the athlete gracefully clears the bar by tucking their takeoff leg under their body. Although this technique may not significantly enhance bar clearance compared to the eastern cut-off, it does not demand extensive flexibility. The main advantage is that it assists a greater number of athletes in successfully clearing the bar.

➢ Straddle Technique

In this technique the athlete clears the bar with facing down and the body stretched along the bar. In straddle technique the part of the leg is lower than the bar at the peak of the jump. This allows the pelvis to rise to a greater height with improved effectiveness of the bar clearance.

Pole vault

Pole Vault has been a medal event at the Olympic Games since 1896 for men and 2000 for women. In the pole vault, you sprint down a track, plant one end of the pole in the metal box, and catapult yourself over a 4.5m horizontal bar (without knocking it to the ground), release the pole, and fall onto the landing mattress. The pole can be of any length, diameter and made of any material, but the basic rules and technique state that you must not move your hands along the pole when it is upright; you must clear the bar feet first, and twist so that your stomach faces the bar, as you descend.

Here are some terminologies used in pole vault.

Bar - The crossbar that is suspended above the ground where athletes have to vault across.

Pit - The mats used for landing in pole vault.

Pole - Usually made of fibreglass and stiffer on one side to allow the pole to bend after planting it to the ground.

UNIT-IV

Technical training and practice of following events:-

Sprints starting techniques
Sprinters begin the race by assuming a crouching position in the starting blocks before driving forward and gradually moving into an upright position as the race progresses and momentum is gained. The set position differs depending on the start.

Sprints finishing techniques
1. Run through: This technique is generally adopted by novice athletes. In this technique, the finishing line is crossed with the full speed by the athletes.
2. Lunging: In this technique, the athlete bends his 'torso' towards the finishing line in the last stride. This technique is adopted by experienced or well experienced athletes.
3. Shoulder shrug: An athlete tends to bend his one shoulder and the complete action is performed in the last stride near the finishing line by the extraordinary athletes.

Shot put (Basic Teaching Stages)
Teach your athletes the fundamental sequence needed to maximize the shot put:-

- Build good footwork and balance in your throwers to increase momentum and throwing distance while reducing errors.
- Learn a simple pivoting drill that focuses on weight distribution, heel placement and finishing with full extension that is the basis for an explosive finish.
- Discover how to master the three positions in the shot put.

Discus throw (Basic Teaching Stages)
The main objective of the thrower is to concentrate on the rhythm. Focusing on the rhythm can bring about the consistency required to execute a perfect throw. Moreover, solid technique and balance are essential factors in determining how long the throw goes. Initially, the thrower sets up their

position in the center of the circle with the weight distributed equally over both of his/her feet. They may also crouch to get that extra edge and momentum. Precise balance is required as linear movement combined with a one-and-a-half rotation.

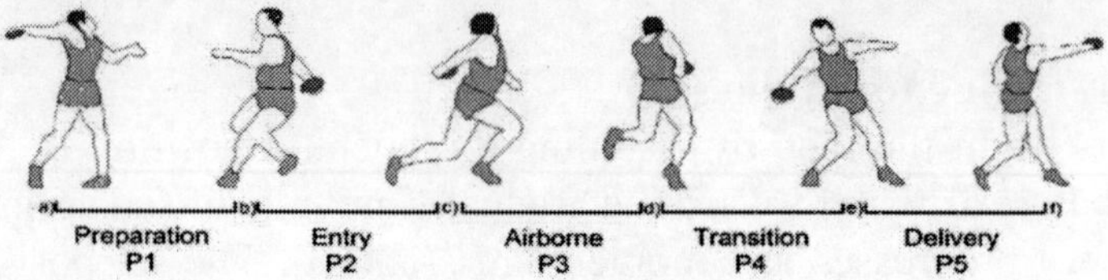

The next stage is moving the weight over the appropriate foot and running the circle. The end objective is landing on that power position which helps propel the discus. The foot should be in the center and the h

Javelin throw (Basic Teaching Stages)

- Stand sideways on, looking in the direction you are throwing.
- Hold the beanbag high and behind the shoulder line with the palm turned up.
- Hold the non-throwing arm in front of the body.
- Keep the opposite foot to the throwing arm forward.
- The weight of the body is on the back leg which should be bent.
- The arm is pulled through with the elbow leading to the palm.
- Pull back the non-throwing arm as the throwing arm comes through.
- Transfer the weight of the body from the back to the front leg as you release the beanbag.

Long Jump (Basic Teaching Stages)

- Speed Phase

Teach the jumper how to run properly with appropriate arm and leg action. The arms should swing from the shoulder joint limiting the shrug action which is common in young sprinters.

- The take-off

The take-off is the transition from the final step to being airborne. An athlete needs to ensure that their foot is flat on the ground to have optimum impact as jumping off either the heels or the toes has adverse impacts on the jump.

- The final six steps

In this stage we will have the jumper back up so his approach will be 6 total steps (3 on the take off leg). We will find which leg he is most comfortable with for the take off. We then work on trying to get the penultimate step concept.

- Hitting the board and finding an approach length

In this stage we spend time teaching the jumper to get consistent on hitting the board.

Triple Jump (Basic Teaching Stages)

- Start the jump before the board. If they go over the foul line on the take-off board, the attempt will be discarded as a foul.
- When jumping, the athlete must land on the same foot used to take-off.

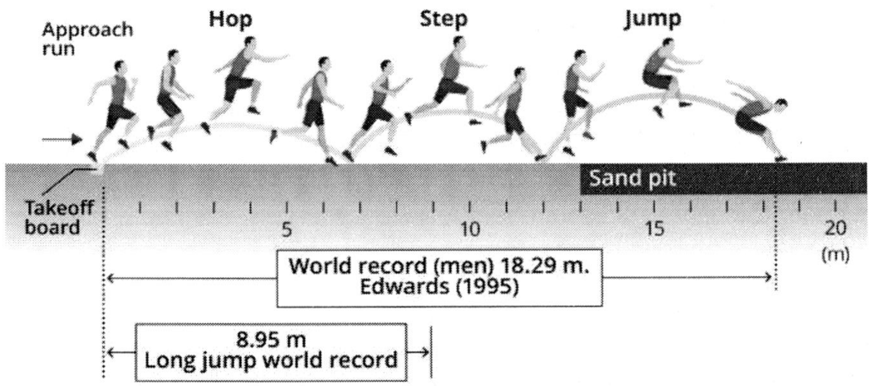

- During the second phase, the athlete must land on the opposing foot and initiate the third phase of the jump.
- The athlete can land in the sand.
- The measured distance will be measured from the closest mark in the sand to the take-off point.

High Jump (Basic Teaching Stages)
The high jump technique is divided into the following phases;

- Approach
- Take-off
- Bar clearance
- Landing

Off the four stages, the take-off is the most important.

Pole vault (Basic Teaching Stages)
Pole vaulting is growing in popularity all over the world due to an increase in track and field programs. The sport requires a high level of bodily awareness, flexibility, and speed.

The pole vault event consists of these phases:
1. The vaulter stands at the end of the runway holding the pole vertically.
2. The runner sprints along the runway as the top of the pole is moved towards the ground.
3. The pole is planted in the box.
4. The pole flexes and absorbs the energy of the runner.
5. The pole straightens and the runner is propelled up and over the bar.

Calculations of Straight, Radius and Staggers of Standard Tracks

Stagger is a word used in athletics. It is only used in track events. Stagger is the change in starting line of the lanes for the events that include curve running. Staggers are used to making the distance between the starting line and end line fair and equal for all participants. Stagger is the excess distance covered by the runners from 2nd lane to 8th lane, on their running path in one lap, when compared to the distance covered by the first lane runner on his running path in one lap. The formula to find out the stagger for standard track = [(w * (n-1))-0.10] * 2π. And for non-standard track = w* (n-1) * 2π. (w=Width of Lane, n= Lane Number)

Relays

Relay race is an event where a team of four athletes run equal predetermined distances in a sprint race, each passing a rod-like object called the 'baton' to the next person to continue the race. The last runner in a relay is called the 'anchor'.

Holding of the baton and various types of baton exchange

Baton change can be divided into three types, namely inside pass, outside pass and the mixed pass based on the side of the body from which the receiver takes the baton. In relay races, baton change is done in two ways, namely the visual pass and the non-visual pass, as appropriate for the event.

References

- Thomas MacMillan (April 30, 2012). "On State Street, "Maker" Movement Arrives". New Haven Independent.
- "Makers UPV: making locally, winning globally | Startup Europe". startupeuropeclub.eu. Archived from the original on 2016-08-21. Retrieved 2016-08-12.
- Martinez, Sylvia (2013). Invent To Learn. Torrance, CA: Constructing Modern Knowledge. pp. 32–35. ISBN 978-0-9891511-0-8.
- "Video games as performance art".
- History of Drawing. From Dibujos para Pintar. Archived 2010-11-20 at the Wayback Machine Retrieved 23 October 2009.
- "Drawing". History.com. 2006. Archived from the original on 14 March 2009. Retrieved 23 October 2009.
- Pinsker, Joe (2019-09-19). "Why Some People Become Lifelong Readers". The Atlantic. Retrieved 2019-10-02.
- History of Painting. From History World. Retrieved 23 October 2009.
- "ISAPA 2021 Goes Online". 2 November 2020.
- "Symposia". IFAPA.
- "New Zealand and Mooven to co-organize the International Symposium on Adapted Physical Activity July 2023". 31 August 2020.
- "ASAPE". www.asape.net. Retrieved 2024-03-24.
- "European Federation of Adapted Physical Activity". European Federation of Adapted Physical Activity.
- "ABOUT NAFAPA". nafapa.
- "Inicio". FeSAFA.
- Pérez, J.; Reina, R.; Sanz, D. (2012). "Adapted Physical Activity for people with disability in Spain: scientific perspectives and current issues". CCD. Cultura_Ciencia_Deporte. 72 (21): 213–224. doi:10.12800/ccd.v7i21.86.
- "APE definition". Retrieved 23 January 2021.

- Dunn, J.; Leitschuh, C. (2010). Special physical education. Kendall Hunt Publishing.
- DePauw, K. (2020). Historical viewpoint in adapted physical education. In J. Haegele, S. Hodge, & D. R. Shapiro (Eds.), Routledge Handbook of Adapted Physical Education. Routledge, Taylor & Francis Group.
- Temenoff, J.S.; Mikos, A.G. (2008). Biomaterials : the Intersection of biology and materials science (Internat. ed.). Upper Saddle River, N.J.: Pearson/Prentice Hall. ISBN 978-0-13-009710-1.
- Totten, George E.; Liang, Hong, eds. (2004). Mechanical tribology : materials, characterization, and applications. New York: Marcel Dekker. ISBN 978-0-8247-4873-9.
- Waite, Lee; Fine, Jerry (2007). Applied biofluid mechanics. New York: McGraw-Hill. ISBN 978-0-07-147217-3.
- Young, Donald F.; Bruce R. Munson; Theodore H. Okiishi (2004). A brief introduction to fluid mechanics (3rd ed.). Hoboken, N.J.: Wiley. ISBN 978-0-471-45757-2.
- "Experimental pedagogy and experimental psychology". psycnet.apa.org. APA PsycNet. Retrieved 2024-02-07.
- Jahrling R (1923). "Experimental Pedagogy, the Science of Education". The Pedagogical Seminary. 30 (1): 40–44. doi:10.1080/08919402.1923.10532906. ISSN 0891-9402.
- Deines AG (2019), "Experimental Pedagogy: The Connection Between Teaching and Social Impact", Teaching and Designing in Detroit, Routledge, doi:10.4324/9780429290596-10, ISBN 978-0-429-29059-6, retrieved 2024-02-07
- Williams, Gavin. "Socrates in Stellenbosch and Tutorials in Oxford." Paper presented at the Tutorial Education: History, Pedagogy, and Evolution conference, Lawrence University, Appleton, WI, 31 March – 1 April 2007. See [1] Archived 2011-07-26 at the Wayback Machine
- "Understanding the Socratic Method of Teaching". Abraham Lincoln University. 10 February 2020. Archived from the original on 1 November 2020. Retrieved 22 August 2021.

- Smith A (1922). Ernst Meumann as the Founder of Experimental Pedagogy: A Comparative, Critical Historical Study. New York University, Graduate School of Arts and Science.
- "Sideline Officials". Archived from the original on 2019-01-23. Retrieved 2019-01-22.
- "The Rules of Flat Track Roller Derby – Women's Flat Track Derby Association". Wftda.com. Archived from the original on 2016-01-28. Retrieved 2016-07-18.
- Alterman, Marcia; Powell, Joan (2016). Women's Volleyball Officiating Manual. Oxford, KS: Professional Association of Volleyball Officials.
- Malcolm Fare. "THE DEVELOPMENT OF FENCING WEAPONS". Archived from the original on 2021-02-24. Retrieved 2021-03-13.
- "The Amateur Game – Global and Going Places". Sumo Fan Magazine. No. 6. April 2006. Retrieved August 5, 2023.
- Rosenberg, Aaron; Dupuis, Ann; Houle, Melissa (2005). The Deryni NextAdventure Game. Grey Ghost Press, Inc. p. 106. ISBN 978-1-887154-09-3.
- Jones, Rebecca J.; Woods, Stephen A.; Guillaume, Yves R. F. (June 2016). "The effectiveness of workplace coaching: a meta-analysis of learning and performance outcomes from coaching" (PDF). Journal of Occupational and Organizational Psychology. 89 (2): 249–277. doi:10.1111/joop.12119.
- Lorber, Laura (10 April 2008). "Executive Coaching – Worth the Money?". The Wall Street Journal. Retrieved 12 November 2008.
- Wang, Yanfei; Yuan, Chuqin (2017). "Coaching leadership and employee voice behavior: a multilevel study". Social Behavior and Personality. 45 (10): 1655–1664. doi:10.2224/sbp.6593.
- Gyllensten, Kristina; Palmer, Stephen (July 2005). "Can coaching reduce workplace stress?". The Coaching Psychologist. 1: 15–17. CiteSeerX 10.1.1.465.4855. doi:10.53841/bpstcp.2005.1.1.15. S2CID 255930948.
- "Definition of Christian Coaching" (PDF).